ABOUT T

MARYON STEWART

Maryon Stewart studied preventive de........nd nutrition at the Royal Dental Hospital in London and worked as a counsellor with nutritional doctors in England for four years. At the beginning of 1984, she set up the PMT Advisory Service which has subsequently helped thousands of women worldwide. In 1987, she launched the Women's Nutritional Advisory Service (WNAS) which now provides broader help to women of all ages.

Maryon is the author of the bestselling books BEAT PMS THROUGH DIET, now in its third edition, and BEAT SUGAR CRAVING; she is the co-author of THE VITALITY DIET and BEAT IBS THROUGH DIET. She has had her own weekly radio programme on health and nutrition, she has co-written several medical papers and has written articles for many glossy magazines including *Marie Claire, Cosmopolitan, Chat, Woman's Journal, BBC Good Health, Woman's Own,* and for the *Daily Mirror.* She has also appeared on several popular TV magazine shows, including *TV AM, GMTV Top of the Morning, Channel Four Food File, BBC Here & Now, Good Morning with Anne & Nick, Reportage, The Miriam Stoppard Health and Beauty Show, This Morning, Pebble Mill, Channel Four Streetwise* and programmes on Meridian, Carlton, BSkyB and TVS. She has contributed regularly to *Capital Woman,* has done a series of programmes for Yorkshire TV's *Help Yourself* programmes and has helped Anglia TV with their *Bodyworks* series. She has written her own regular page in the magazine *House and Garden* and she now writes regularly for *Health and Fitness* magazine. She frequently lectures to both the lay public and medical profession. She is married to Dr Alan Stewart and they live in Lewes, Sussex, with their four children.

SARAH TOOLEY

Sarah trained as a nurse in Sussex. After leaving the NHS in 1984 she joined the PMT Advisory Service shortly after its birth (now the WNAS). For eight years she was senior nurse at the WNAS where she gave nutritional advice to women in her WNAS clinics in London and Hove as well as postal advice to women on a national and international basis. Sarah has worked closely with Maryon, co-writing medical papers, running research trials and previously making major contributions to the menu and recipe sections of THE VITALITY DIET and BEAT PMS THROUGH DIET books.

Sarah now works full-time as a nutrition consultant. She regularly writes articles on nutrition and also an advice page for *Nature's Best* magazine and is studying part-time for an honours degree. Sarah has given over 100 radio interviews and lectures, to the lay public and medical profession, on the subject of PMS, menopause and nutrition and has appeared on television on several occasions.

Also by Maryon Stewart:

Beat PMS Through Diet
The Vitality Diet
Beat Sugar Craving
Beat IBS Through Diet
Beat Menopause Without HRT

BEAT PMS COOKBOOK

Over 100 tempting recipes based on
the bestselling *Beat PMS Through Diet*

Maryon Stewart
with Sarah Tooley

VERMILION
LONDON

To Phoebe, Hester, Betsy, Faye and Chesca
– the young women of tomorrow.

First published in the United Kingdom in 1990 by Ebury Press

This edition published in 1995 by Vermilion, an imprint of Ebury Press
Random House
20 Vauxhall Bridge Road
London SW1V 2SA

Copyright © 1990 and 1995 by Maryon Stewart with Sarah Tooley

The right of Maryon Stewart and Sarah Tooley to be identified
as the authors of this work has been asserted by them in accordance with the Copyright,
Designs and Patents Act 1988.

Random House Australia (Pty) Limited
10 Alfred Street, Milsons Point, Sydney
New South Wales 2061, Australia

Random House New Zealand Limited
18 Poland Road, Glenfield
Auckland 10, New Zealand

Random House South Africa (Pty) Limited
PO Box 337, Bergvlei, South Africa

Random House UK Limited Reg. No. 954009

A CIP catalogue record for this book is available from the British Library.

ISBN 0 09 180664 X

Phototypeset by Textype Typesetters, Cambridge
Printed and bound in Great Britain by Mackays of Chatham, plc, Kent

CONTENTS

IMPORTANT NOTE FOR SUFFERERS

If you have symptoms which occur at other times of the month, apart from during your pre-menstrual time, you should have a medical check-up with your own doctor. If your symptoms are very severe it would be advisable to have your nutritional programme supervised by your own doctor or a trained counsellor. If you get confused or need extra advice, the Women's Nutritional Advisory Service is there to help you. All letters receive a personal reply: their address is on page 207. For further information about the WNAS and its services, please send a large self-addressed envelope and four separate first class stamps indicating which pack you wish to receive.

ACKNOWLEDGEMENTS

We would like to thank Dr Guy Abraham and Dr Alan Stewart for their pioneering work in the field of nutrition and PMS, which has made our job so much easier.

Thanks are also due to Lavinia Trevor for her guidance, and to Joanna Sheehan and Amelia Thorpe at Ebury Press for their professionalism and enthusiasm.

This book would not have been possible without the wonderful feedback we have had over the years from our patients far and wide.

We are grateful to Jenny Tooley for her typing skills, Jane Booker for caring for the children whilst we worked, and Michele Apsey, Cheryl Griffiths and Mike Davenport for their help. We would also like to acknowledge and thank the dedicated team of 'girls' at the Women's Nutritional Advisory Service for their hard teamwork and support over the years.

INTRODUCTION

It is an established fact that dietary factors are closely related to our health. It is accepted that dietary changes can prevent heart disease, and play a major role in the control of diabetes and kidney disease. Experts now agree that the nutritional approach to Pre-Menstrual Syndrome, or PMS as it is more commonly known, is the best first-line treatment. In other words, by making dietary changes it is possible that you can alleviate your PMS symptoms to a large degree.

What is not widely known, or appreciated, is just how one goes about making dietary changes, and what specific changes to the diet need to be made in order to overcome the different types of symptoms that women experience. For example, the dietary recommendations for overcoming breast tenderness would be somewhat different from the recommendations that would help abdominal bloating or irritability.

The Women's Nutritional Advisory Service has been giving dietary advice to women all over the world since 1984. The WNAS, formerly the PMT Advisory Service, has personally helped over fifty thousand women overcome their symptoms using the nutritional approach. From a study of two hundred WNAS patients, it was established that 96.5 per cent of the patients felt significantly better after the initial three months of following the recommendations. The WNAS programme is detailed in the successful companion to this book *Beat PMS Through Diet*.

This book concentrates on the different types of dietary changes that apply to the various types of symptoms. It is based on the extensive first-hand experience that we have gained from working with the women who over the years have come to us for help at the WNAS.

This special cookbook is designed to help you to help yourself. If this is your first encounter with the nutritional approach to PMS, you will need to read through the diet section and pick out the diet that is recommended for the majority of your symptoms. If you suffer with more than one category of symptoms you will need to combine several sets of recommendations initially. Read the book once through first, and then go back to the relevant sections to pick out the dietary recommendations most suitable for you. If you would like some personal help please write to the Women's Nutritional Advisory Service, PO Box 268, Lewes, East Sussex BN7 2QN (Telephone 0273 487366). Please enclose a large self-addressed envelope and four separate first-class stamps.

If you have read *Beat PMS Through Diet*, or have in fact been on the WNAS programme, you will be able to use this book as a source of further ideas for meal planning. There are menus accompanying each section, and over one hundred recipes in all to choose from.

We wish you well over your symptoms, and hope you enjoy trying the recipes we have selected for you.

PART I

THE PROBLEM

1

PMS – A FORCE TO BE RECKONED WITH

PMS, or more correctly Pre-Menstrual Syndrome, is a collection of symptoms that occur before your period and usually tail off as your period begins. These symptoms usually start between the time you ovulate – when the egg is released by the ovary in the middle of your cycle – and the start of your period. The symptoms occur each month before a period, and classically disappear shortly after the start of the period.

Whilst some fortunate women do not experience any symptoms of PMS, a WNAS survey of women picked at random in the street indicated that some 73.6 per cent of women in Great Britain suffer to some degree. That translates into approximately 10 million women, some 7 million of whom are reckoned to experience moderate or severe pre-menstrual symptoms. So if it's any comfort, you are not suffering alone!

It is only now that we are beginning to realize the extent to which PMS affects the lives of sufferers. In 1992, the WNAS had a study published in the *Research Journal for Complementary Medicine* on a group of 200 patients, all of whom had moderate to severe PMS symptoms. The survey discovered that relationships were commonly affected by symptoms – in fact, 96 per cent of the women surveyed felt that their home life or relationship with their family and friends was affected by their symptoms. Ninety-four per cent of the women felt depressed pre-menstrually, 75 per cent admitted to feeling violent and aggressive before their period, and 91 per cent felt that their productivity and efficiency at work decreased for an average of five days per month. We discovered, very sadly, that of this group 53 per cent had contemplated suicide at least once pre-menstrually, and a staggering 11 per cent had actually attempted suicide at this time. It is quite clear from these statistics that PMS symptoms have a very significant effect on family members as well as on the sufferer herself.

We are often asked why it is that PMS seems to be more common nowadays than in years gone by. To that question there are indeed many answers. PMS has in fact existed for hundreds of years. We probably talk about it far more today, so it is recognized as being a common complaint. However, there are major factors that need to be considered when looking for the causes of PMS symptoms.

First, you must appreciate that our nutritional state today is to some degree an inherited state, one that has been influenced by our physical experiences to date, plus a reflection of our lifestyle to some degree.

THE PRODUCT OF PAST GENERATIONS

People often ask why it is that, although they eat well, they do not feel or look as well as someone they know who drinks, smokes and eats junk food. The fact is that although we can influence our nutritional condition by adjusting our diets now, we are the nutritional product of many generations. Our ancestors' bad habits or inadequate nutritional state can have a direct bearing on what 'material' we each have to start with. There is not a great deal we can do to influence this factor, but it does help to bear it in mind.

THE PHYSICAL CHALLENGE

There is little doubt that physical experiences, especially those of a hormonal nature, take their toll on our bodies, unless of course we are one of the minority of educated individuals who know how to counteract the effects of pregnancy and breastfeeding, for example. We are not taught enough about nutritional requirements in general at school, let alone nutritional requirements for special situations. In fact we tend to know more about the needs of our cars than those of our bodies.

There are increased nutritional requirements during pregnancy and again during breastfeeding. If these are not adequately met, then the nutrients are passed from the mother's body to the infant. Over a period of time the mother then suffers lowered levels of certain key nutrients. When the body has borderline levels of important nutrients, or it in fact becomes deficient, it cannot function in an optimum fashion; conditions like PMS then occur even in women who may not previously have experienced them. Repeating this scenario in the second and possibly third pregnancy only serves to make the matter worse. Thus it is not uncommon to hear that PMS becomes worse after the second or third pregnancy.

NUTRITIONAL STATE INFLUENCES HORMONE LEVELS

Research now shows us that nutritional factors can influence hormone levels in the body and brain chemical metabolism. To this day doctors fail to agree on the actual cause of PMS. Many feel that it is due to a hormone imbalance – probably low levels of the hormone progesterone. However, some others think that it may be to do with the hormone oestrogen; whilst yet others consider that PMS is a disturbance of brain chemicals. Doctors often give hormone therapy in order to overcome the PMS symptoms, but what they are actually doing is masking the symptoms. For when the hormone treatment ceases, the symptoms return.

With the nutritional approach we are looking for the actual cause of the symptoms. Once we have found the cause we then address the problem and correct it by replacing the vitamins and minerals that are in short supply, so that the symptoms are eliminated on a permanent basis without having to resort to drugs at all, either in the short or long term.

This balance of hormones is affected by the ovaries, the liver and by normal bowel function.

Vitamin B and the type of diet we eat are also important. Vitamin B appears to be necessary in the breakdown of oestrogen by the liver. Together with the minerals zinc and magnesium vitamin B also influences tissues, such as the lining of the womb's response to oestrogen.

The balance of fibre and fat in the diet can affect the level of oestrogen in the blood.

Changing from an average western diet to a diet high in fibre and low in saturated (animal) fats can lower oestrogen levels. This may be desirable for women with PMS and especially for those with breast problems.

Improving your diet can help to regulate hormone levels and improve brain metabolism which is what is needed in order to overcome PMS in the long term.

TWENTIETH-CENTURY LIFESTYLE

For many of us the twentieth century has brought a distinct change in lifestyle. We no longer have the extended family to fall back on, and we are often expected to go out to work as well as run a home and care for children. From time to time we may well experience stressful situations, like moving house, difficulties with children, financial or marital problems, or indeed just the stress of life in the fast lane.

Stress has an adverse effect on the body. It may even place

increased nutritional demands on the body. Additionally, if we are overstretched and harassed we are far more likely to rely on pre-prepared processed food rather than indulging in home cooking, or we may indeed even eat sweet food in excess as a comfort. These types of foods contain less in the way of good nutrients, and in some cases even block the absorption of good nutrients from other foods.

It is also likely that when time is short, and we are overburdened, we have less time to exercise regularly. Exercise is very important. It has a proven beneficial effect – especially in helping to overcome symptoms of depression, anxiety and fatigue. Exercising is one of the few natural ways to speed up your metabolism, which is a very important consideration if you tend to put on weight. Regular exercise also is an excellent way to improve your general feeling of wellbeing.

2

UPTIGHT, BLOATED AND DEPRESSED?

Pre-Menstrual Syndrome is a rather unusual condition as there are so many different sorts of symptoms that may be associated with it – it is thought that there are possibly in the region of 150. Most sufferers experience a few of the symptoms on a regular basis, and perhaps a few other symptoms some months, but not necessarily every month.

At WNAS we use a system of classifying symptoms which was devised by Dr Guy Abraham, a former professor of obstetrics and gynaecology from the University of California in Los Angeles. This classification works quite well, and helps us to some extent to select the type of diet and nutritional supplements that would be most suitable. There are four main groups of symptoms. Put a tick against the symptoms that you suffer on a regular basis:

GROUP A (Anxiety)

	Tick
Nervous tension	——
Mood swings	——
Irritability	——
Anxiety	——

GROUP H (Hydration)

Weight gain
Swelling of extremities ___
Breast tenderness ___
Abdominal bloating ___

GROUP C (Cravings)

Headache ___
Craving for sweets ___
Increased appetite ___
Heart pounding ___
Fatigue ___

GROUP D (Depression)

Depression ___
Forgetfulness ___
Crying ___
Confusion ___
Insomnia ___

It is possible that all of your symptoms fell into one group – but is unlikely. It is very common to suffer symptoms from more than one group, and indeed many women suffer symptoms from all four groups. Before deciding on the type of diet you should follow you will need to complete the following questionnaire. Your answers to the questions will give you the key to which dietary recommendations you should be following.

SYMPTOM QUESTIONNAIRE

1.   Are most of your symptoms mild? (Score one)   Score
(*Mild is defined as symptoms present that you are aware of,
but they do not prevent you from carrying out all your usual
activities.*)

2.   Are most of your symptoms moderate? (Score three)
(*Moderate is defined as symptoms present that change the
way you feel to the point where you occasionally cancel
arrangements, and the family usually know your period is
coming before you do.*)

3.   Are many of your symptoms severe? (Score six)
(*Severe is defined as life-shattering symptoms. When they
occur you are unable to carry on with your usual routine –
in fact, you feel quite unable to cope until the symptoms
have passed.*)

Score three for a yes to each of the following questions:

4.   Would you describe yourself as Jekyll and Hyde
(like two different people), one before your period and
another after your period has begun?

5.   Do you find it difficult to control your emotions
when your symptoms are present?

6.   Do you feel that your symptoms are spoiling your
relationship with your partner or your children?

7.   Do you feel that your symptoms affect your efficiency or productivity at work?

8.   Do you find life generally difficult to cope with
before your period arrives?

Total score   ____

DID YOU SCORE THREE OR UNDER?

If you scored three or less you will almost certainly only need to follow the diet designed for mild sufferers. It seems that your PMS problems are under control, but you will probably benefit generally from the dietary changes. Refer to page 61 for your recommendations.

DID YOU SCORE SIX OR UNDER?

You fall into the category of a moderate sufferer. You will need to make the specific dietary changes that are outlined on page 70. In addition you may be advised to take some of the recommended nutritional supplements, which you can read about on page 53.

DID YOU SCORE SEVEN OR MORE?

You are obviously suffering severe symptoms. You will need to answer the next set of questions very carefully, and then follow the dietary recommendations beginning on page 80. You will need to take the recommended nutritional supplements for at least six months to help boost the nutritional levels in your body.

FURTHER QUESTIONS FOR SEVERE SUFFERERS

1. Do you suffer regularly with any two or more of the following symptoms pre-menstrually? (Score one for each)

Score

   Abdominal bloating
   Excessive wind
   Constipation
   Diarrhoea
   Depression
   Mouth ulcers
   Fatigue

If you scored more than two in this section, you will need to follow the specific recommendations for a wheat-restricted diet on page 36.

2. Do you suffer any of the following symptoms? (Score one for each)

Score

Itchy bottom
Bloated abdomen
Cracking at the corners of your mouth
Depression
Excessive wind
Cystitis

Have you had more than two episodes of thrush in the last five years?

If you scored more than two in this section, or if you have had more than two episodes of thrush in the last five years, you will need to follow the recommendations for a yeast-restricted diet on page 39.

3. Would you describe mood swings and irritability as being two symptoms that you suffer especially severely? If the answer is yes, you will need to pay special attention to the extra recommendations on page 44.

4. Do you suffer severe breast tenderness for at least three to four days, practically every month, before your period begins? If your answer to this question is yes, you will need to pay particular attention to the extra recommendations on page 48.

5. (a) Does your desire to eat sweet foods increase pre-menstrually?
(b) Does your consumption of sweet foods or drinks at least double pre-menstrually?

If the answer to either of these questions is yes, you will need to follow the special recommendations on page 40 as well.

6. (a) Is your only pre-menstrual symptom depression? In other words, do you experience depression and not other symptoms before your period is due?

(b) Does your depression occur all through the month practically every day of your menstrual cycle (from the day your period begins until your next period is due)?

If the answer to either of the above questions is yes, you will need to follow the advice given on page 46.

PART II

THE DIET

3

A LITTLE KNOWLEDGE
GOES A LONG WAY

For hundreds of years the knowledge that we have acquired about diet has been passed down from generation to generation. Different cultures obviously had different views on what the optimum diets were, but the information was at best intuitive, rather than scientifically based. Today we are very fortunate in that we have the scientific ability to determine what a good diet actually is. We can measure the harm that poor-quality foods bring about, and we can measure the value of good food to the body.

Before doing another weekly shop it is important to understand how the food and drink that you are about to consume might affect you. Obviously you will shop according to your taste and your pocket, and to some degree according to the traditions that have been set by your family. But there are certain groups of foods that should get a special mention right here at the outset as there clearly seems to be a relationship between them and adverse symptoms. These relationships are dealt with in greater detail in Chapter 4.

ANIMAL FAT

It is widely recognized that our diet contains too much animal fat, which is often known as saturated fat. Animal fat is associated with heart disease, obesity and breast cancer. It also seems to aggravate many of the PMS symptoms. A study published in the *British Medical Journal* showed that a reduced animal fat diet and one which was high in fruit and vegetable fibre reduced benign (non-malignant) breast disease, including pre-menstrual breast tenderness. Animal fat should be replaced with polyunsaturated fat – cold-pressed oils such as sunflower or safflower, and spreads such as Flora.

FIBRE

In general our diets are too low in the right sort of fibre. The fibre we have been brainwashed to regard as healthful is bran. But we now know that bran blocks the absorption of several essential minerals, and aggravates many abdominal symptoms like bloating, wind, constipation and diarrhoea. You will be far better off increasing your consumption of salad, vegetables and fruit, all of which contain good amounts of vitamins and minerals. If bran is currently your solution to constipation, you can replace it with a daily dose of linseeds. These are available from health food shops in the form of Linusit Gold. One to two tablespoons of linseeds with fruit and a little yogurt makes a delicious breakfast or snack and will more than adequately replace the laxative function of bran.

SALT

We use between ten and twenty times more salt than our bodies actually require. Salt consumption is directly related to water retention in the body and to high blood pressure. If you are an addict, to start with you will need to use a replacement product like LoSalt, but as soon as possible try to stop using salt altogether in your cooking or at the table, especially if you are prone to retain water pre-menstrually.

SUGAR

In the UK alone we consume about 36 kg (80 lb) of sugar each per year. Apart from craving sweet food, we eat all sorts of food that contains hidden sugar. Sugar too promotes water retention in the body, and for this reason as well as many others is best avoided. It is a food that is empty of good nutrients, and in fact excessive consumption of sweet food may even impede the absorption of these nutrients.

TEA, COFFEE AND COLA-BASED DRINKS

Tea, coffee and cola-based drinks contain high levels of caffeine and tannin. Both of these compounds are known to block the absorption of many essential nutrients. They are all addictive drinks which exacerbate symptoms of anxiety, nervous tension, insomnia and breast tenderness. Each mug of tea contains approximately 120 mgs of caffeine, each mug of instant coffee about 150 mgs and each mug of filter coffee contains a staggering 250 mgs of caffeine. An intake in excess of 250 mg of caffeine per day can cause many adverse symptoms. We therefore recommend that tea and coffee should be reduced to a maximum of two or three cups per day, preferably a decaffeinated variety, and an alternative like Rooibosch 11 o'clock Tea, Barley Cup and dandelion coffee should be used instead.

If you suffer anxiety, irritability, mood swings, nervous tension, insomnia or breast tenderness it is really advisable for you to give up these drinks altogether. If you are used to drinking several cups a day you may well experience headaches, irritability and even mild shakes as you attempt to eliminate them from your diet. These symptoms, if they occur, will pass within a week or two at the most – maybe even within a few days. On page 96 you will find a list of pleasant alternative drinks to try. Keep an open mind as you work your way through the list. You will be amazed at how quickly your tastes adapt once you have made the decision to make the changes.

JUNK FOOD

Processed foods and TV dinners are promoted as a fast and convenient alternative to home cooking. It is easy to see how the glossy promotion of fast foods makes them attractive to many of us who have very busy lifestyles or who simply prefer the easy way out. Unfortunately, the processing of these meals greatly reduces the vitamin and mineral content of the basic ingredients. When eaten on a regular basis, these foods may even prevent good nutrients from other foods from being absorbed.

MEAT

Although red meat was regarded by our ancestors as being one of the best – if not *the* best – type of food to consume, we now know that it should be consumed in moderation. The type of red meat available to us today is often too fatty, and may well have been contaminated with crop spray, antibiotics, even, possibly, growth hormones, all of which are undesirable to our bodies. Meat infected with BSE, better known as mad cow disease, still continues to be a worry. You will probably feel a great deal better if you limit your intake of red meat to a maximum of three portions of organic or additive-free meat per week. Better still, eat free-range chicken and fish instead.

Additive-free meat is available from many butchers, and can sometimes be bought directly from a farm shop. Wild fish is preferable to farmed fish. Free-range eggs are a far better option than battery or other eggs which often contain antibiotics and could be contaminated with salmonella.

ADDITIVES

Our bodies were not designed to cope with many of the chemical additives in the form of artificial colourings, stabilizers, flavour enhancers and preservatives that are now found in many of our foods. Whilst some are not harmful, the long-term effects of many of them on the human body are unknown. It is far better to avoid additives wherever possible.

OTHER ENVIRONMENTAL FACTORS

The Ministry of Agriculture, Fisheries and Food has admitted that 99 per cent of all fruit and vegetables are treated at least once with some form of crop spray. There are many known environmental factors that can affect our food – anything from insecticides to nitrates in the soil or lead in petrol to airborne pollution. Apart from actively campaigning to lessen these harmful factors over the years, there is little we can do on a day-to-day basis other than learning how to choose the best food possible.

Organically grown fruit and vegetables are preferable to those that have been chemically sprayed. These are now available in many supermarkets. But nothing tastes better than home-grown produce – so if you have space in your garden or access to a plot of land, invest in a book on organic gardening (see page 202) and get to work. If you haven't the time to garden yourself, try to persuade a friend or relative to do the work in exchange for your supplying the materials. You can then share the produce.

SOCIAL POISONS

Sadly, many of our social habits also affect our nutritional state. For example, alcohol blocks the absorption of most good nutrients, and should be avoided where possible. The maximum allowance of alcohol is three units per week, in other words three glasses of wine, or three measures of spirit, or three half pints of beer or lager. If you suffer particularly with breast tenderness, migraine or insomnia it would be worth cutting out alcohol altogether for at least an initial three-month period.

The social poisons also cover tobacco, drugs and even tea and coffee. It might amaze you to know that for every £1 spent on food in the UK, 76p is spent on alcohol and tobacco!

DRINKING WATER

Disturbingly, it is now accepted that drinking water in many areas contains pollutants which are undesirable and often harmful to our bodies in the long term. The quality of the drinking water in many parts of the UK does not meet World Health Organization standards, particularly with regard to the high levels of lead and nitrates that are present. A slow accumulation of lead may affect child development and intelligence, and the nitrates are thought to increase the risk of cancer. It makes great sense to invest in an efficient water filter, which can be plumbed into the mains by your kitchen tap. A good water purifier will remove the vast majority of the harmful elements from the water.

THE LAST STRAW

It is very disheartening to realize that even after going to all the trouble of growing your own vegetables and buying additive-free food, the cooking process destroys up to half the vitamins and mineral content of the food. It is just one of those facts that must be taken into account when planning balanced meals and menus. Grilling and steaming food causes less nutritional loss than frying, boiling and baking. It makes good sense to eat as much raw food as possible in order to get the full nutritional benefit. Plenty of salads, raw or lightly steamed vegetables and fruit will help to build up your vitamin and mineral intake.

THE PAY-OFF

Whilst we admit that it does take time and effort to ring the changes, if you are sufficiently interested in your own health, and in the health and welfare of your family, you should have all the incentive you are likely to need. Some people like to start by making gradual changes; others prefer to make a clean sweep. Make the changes in the way that you feel you could best cope with and stick to in the long term. Changing long-standing habits is not an easy task, but it is not an impossible task either, especially when you have the vested interest of overcoming your symptoms as well as becoming more healthy generally.

4

THE NUTRITIONAL PROGRAMME THAT CHANGES LIVES

When we set out in 1984 to help women overcome their PMS, we had little idea about the workability and effectiveness of the nutritional programme. We knew from published medical literature that specific nutritional supplements and dietary changes would help alleviate symptoms to some degree. It was not until we saw women completing their nutritional programme that we began to realize just how effective this method of treatment was.

As time went on we realized that we were transforming even the most desperate and suicidal PMS sufferers back into normal, balanced, happy human beings. Women who had previously described themselves as 'Jekyll and Hyde' were claiming that they felt stable all month and better than they could remember feeling since their youth. Husbands wrote to us gratefully claiming that they had 'got back the girl they married'. Many broken relationships 'mended', and very often found a new lease of life, once the woman was over her symptoms. Women, with reports verified by their husbands, claimed that their previously disminished or non-existent sex drive had risen to new improved levels.

Children stopped being afraid of their mothers, wondering whether they were about to lash out – although most of them spent many a nervous month watching carefully and waiting for mum to change back into an irrational monster. Women who had previously been afraid to work had successfully taken on responsible jobs outside the home. Even those who had previously suffered from agoraphobia for as long as ten years, as well as PMS, were now making regular solo outings to visit the hairdressers and the shops. Many women who had previously become dependent on tranquillizers or anti-depressants were managing to stop their medication, under the supervision of their doctors, without experiencing withdrawal symptoms.

The 'magic' continued as the years rolled on. In the first analysis of the nutritional programme, we found that 79 per cent of the women felt that their symptoms were completely or almost completely gone after three months on the nutritional programme. In a study of two hundred patients in 1990, we found that 96.5 per cent of the women who followed the recommendations felt significantly or completely better within three months. Sadly, one third of the women were non-starters. In a study published in 1995 we discovered our compliance rate had increased by 27% and of the 96% of women who followed the recommendations, 90% were better within 3 months.

The programme we use at the WNAS consists of five key elements:

1. Specific dietary changes according to individual symptoms.
2. Specialized nutritional supplements according to symptoms.
3. Regular 'aerobic' exercise which includes anything from brisk walking, swimming, cycling and jogging to actual aerobic workouts.
4. Lifestyle counselling to address day-to-day living and help to put life back on to an even keel where necessary.
5. The WNAS helpline, which is there to give extra help and advice when necessary.

The programme is designed for moderate to severe patients who are not confident that they can help themselves. It is a four-month course of treatment designed not only to help the woman over her symptoms, but also to arm her with enough education on the subject of diet to carry her through life.

The programme operates from clinics and on a postal and telephone basis for those who are unable to get to a clinic. The postal service has been running successfully for 12 years and has helped women all over the world.

Women who suffer mild to moderate PMS can help themselves with diet, exercise and specific nutritional supplements (see page 53). The WNAS programme is described in some detail in the book *Beat PMS Through Diet*.

NUTRITIONAL DEFICIENCIES

We now know that the underlying cause of PMS is related to nutritional deficiencies.

- Over 50 per cent of women in the UK with PMS have low levels of the mineral magnesium in their red blood cells and magnesium is needed for brain chemical metabolism and normal hormone function.
- Up to 20 per cent of women of child-bearing age in the UK have low iron stores.
- Additionally, B vitamins are often in short supply. A deficiency of B vitamins can lead to psychological disturbance.

With this in mind, women who bear children are put under further nutritional strain during pregnancy and breastfeeding, when the demand for nutrients is at its greatest. Mother Nature ensures that the baby gets what it needs in order to develop, so the good nutrients cross the placenta during pregnancy and go out through the breast milk during feeding, and it is the mother's body that becomes depleted. Improving your nutritional state and redressing the balance is therefore the key to overcoming the symptoms of PMS.

REACTIONS

PMS symptoms can be worsened by certain foods or other external factors, some of which have already been mentioned in passing in Chapter 3.

COFFEE

Heart pounding, nervous tension, irritability, insomnia and diarrhoea.

TEA

Heart pounding, nervous tension, irritability, insomnia and constipation.

ALCOHOL

Headaches, rash, stomach upsets.

MAKE-UP

Itching, dry flaking skin, soreness.

PERFUME

Headaches, rashes.

VARIOUS FOODS (see below)

Abdominal bloating, excessive wind, diarrhoea, constipation, weight gain and other symptoms.

For this reason, when certain symptoms are present it is best to avoid the suspect product or food all month until your PMS symptoms are under control.

SENSITIVITIES

Some PMS symptoms can be worsened by certain foods or external factors and the WNAS programme addresses this.

GRAINS

Among foods, certain grains can be particularly troublesome. A sensitivity to wheat, oats, barley, rye or corn can cause or aggravate the following symptoms: abdominal bloating, excessive wind, constipation, diarrhoea, depression, mouth ulcers and fatigue.

If you experience any of these symptoms exclude wholewheat and wholewheat products from your diet initially. If your symptoms persist, you will need to exclude the other grains too for a period of four weeks. Since corn and rice are the two grains with which women find the least problems, unless you feel they upset you it is fine to include them in your diet initially.

A study of 200 Icelandic postal workers showed that 16% of them produced antibodies to gluten and phytic acid, commonly found in wheat, bran and other grains such as oats, barley and rye to a lesser degree.

In our clinics, at least 50% of our patients seem to experience problems relating to one or more grains initially. When nutrient levels are low, the immune system may be affected and, as a result, may not tolerate certain foods. Added to this we know that 24% of women in the UK experience Irritable Bowel Syndrome.

What to avoid

Wheat   Bread, pasta, cakes, biscuits, pastry, pies, buns, breakfast cereals and sausages.

Oats   Porridge, oat cookies and oat flakes.

Rye   Rye bread (which also contains wheat) and Ryvita.

Barley   Found in packet/tinned soups and stews, and barley beverages.

The rule is to read labels in the supermarket, as flour, modified starch and so on are added to many processed foods.

Assessing for a sensitivity

If you have cut any grains from your diet because you feel you may be allergic to them, avoid whole wheat for six to eight weeks before attempting to reintroduce it; then bring back the grains one at a time. This should be done after your period or in the symptom-free phase of your cycle, so that any possible reaction will not be confused with PMS. Eat your first reintroduced grain at least once or twice a day for five days. If you do not experience any reaction after five days, stop eating that grain and try another one. This introducing phase can take two months or more, depending on the length of your cycle and symptoms.

If you experience a reaction to a particular grain it does not mean that you will never be able to eat this food again – simply that your body is reacting at present. Once your nutritional state has improved, you should find that your body is better able to tolerate this food. It is important to remember, however, that you can be more sensitive when pre-menstrual; therefore there may be some foods that you need to avoid or cut down on at this time of the month until your PMS symptoms have reduced sufficiently.

What to eat instead

- Ener G white or brown rice bread (which tastes good)
- Glutafin wheat-free bread and rolls and Glutafin crackers

- Rice cakes
- Home Baking – potato and rice flour, buckwheat and buckwheat flour
- Pasta – Pastariso and Glutafin
- Rice noodles
- Any rice or corn cereals – Rice Krispies or Cornflakes

Often trial and error are necessary to obtain the correct texture for cooking with these flours. We recommend them if you have established that you have a sensitivity to a particular grain, or in the short term whilst you are avoiding wheat and possibly oats, barley and rye.

Larkhall Laboratories (see page 209) supply Trufree Flours, available from some chemists, which give particularly good results in baking. There is also a very good cookery book called *The Wheat and Gluten-free Cookbook* which gives recipes for using these flours with good results (see Recommended Reading List, page 201).

Nutritional values

You should not lose any nutrients from avoiding these grains for the specified time, as there are many other foods that also supply nutrients. For example:

	Wholemeal bread	Broccoli tops	Soya flour
	mg per 100g		
Fibre	8.5	4.1	14.3
Calcium	23	76	240
Vitamin B6	0.14	0.13	0.68

Following the replacement diet plan above will help you to ensure a well-balanced diet.

The recipes in the recipe section are coded (W) for wholewheat-free and (G) for wheat-, oats-, barley- and rye-free.

You can often substitute a combination of rice flour or cornflour when cooking. For example, 50g (2oz) of each instead of ordinary flour makes an excellent pancake batter using a normal pancake recipe (see page 191).

YEAST

A sensitivity to or excess of yeast can cause these symptoms: itchy bottom, bloated abdomen, cracking at the corners of the mouth, depression, excessive wind, cystitis and thrush.

Yeast is part of the normal make-up of the gut, and is balanced with bacteria to help perform the normal functions of our intestinal tract. Sometimes a yeast overgrowth can occur, causing toxins which can produce mental and physical symptoms. PMS symptoms such as confusion, fatigue, depression, poor memory and a general lethargy and unwell feeling can all be caused or aggravated by a yeast overgrowth. Long illnesses and/or repeated use of antibiotics can also cause the yeast bug to overgrow.

What to avoid

Sugar Sugary foods like cakes, biscuits and honey.

Bread Bread, buns and any foods that have had yeast added to them.

Alcohol Most alcoholic drinks, especially beer, depend on yeast to produce the alcohol.

Juices Citrus fruit juices – only freshly squeezed juice is yeast-free. You can, however, use the small cartons as long as the whole carton is consumed in one sitting. This is because once a large carton is opened yeast begins to form.

Malt Malted cereals and drinks.

Pickles Any pickles, sauerkraut, olives, chillies, vinegar and condiments containing vinegar.

Cheese   Blue cheeses and Brie.

Fungi   Mushrooms.

Fruits   All dried fruits and over-ripe soft fruits.

Extracts   Marmite and stock cubes.

All fermented foods, leftover and stale foods also contain high amounts of yeast. It is very difficult to avoid yeast altogether as it is everywhere around us, but avoiding the above foods until the symptoms subside will help your body to correct its yeast balance. If you feel that your yeast problem is persistent you should consult your GP for oral medication to help.

As live natural yogurt contains bacteria which help to balance the yeast, it may be helpful to eat it two or three times per week.

Vegetable stock used in recipes should be made from the water vegetables have been cooked in which can then be frozen.

To help you follow a low-yeast diet, the menus and recipes in later chapters are coded with a (Y) to indicate that they are suitable for a low-yeast diet.

SUGAR CRAVINGS

Craving for sweet food can be more than just a passing fancy. Very often people get addicted to sweet food, and the problem becomes worse pre-menstrually. It is not uncommon for severe sufferers to consume several chocolate bars per day or even a whole packet of biscuits at one sitting. The body needs sugar in the form of glucose in order for the brain to function and the cells to generate energy. Wholesome food is converted into glucose by the body.

Regular intakes of good food keep the blood sugar levels constant, which in turn keeps cravings for sweet food at bay. But regular 'injections' of refined sweet foods, like cakes, biscuits, sweets, chocolates and the non-diet variety of fizzy drinks, cause the blood sugar levels to rise rapidly and subsequently dip, which then creates a demand for more sweet food.

As refined sweet food is metabolized quickly, it only produces an initial spurt of energy. The sharp lowering of blood sugar is what induces symptoms of hunger, cravings and fatigue. Refined sweet foods are high in calories, but relatively empty of nutrients. They also impede the absorption of nutrients from the good food you may also be eating.

Sweet cravings can be overcome permanently, within a few months. However, it is not an easy task and therefore needs approaching in a very controlled manner. But don't be discouraged – the WNAS has had tremendous success with overcoming sweet cravings and there are many intrinsically sweet foods to eat instead. These our ancestors would have survived on prior to sugar becoming widely available.

EFFECTS OF SUGAR

PMS C – headaches, cravings for sweets, increased appetite, heart pounding, fatigue, and dizziness or fainting. All these symptoms can be associated with poor blood sugar control. Mood swings and irritability are also common reactions.

It is important therefore to maintain good blood sugar control without using refined sugars. This does not mean that you can never eat a piece of chocolate cake again – these things are fine in small quantities once your symptoms have reduced and are under control.

The mineral chromium

It has been found that the trace mineral chromium can play an important role in blood sugar metabolism. Ensure that you are eating a diet rich in chromium by including some of the following foods in your diet: apples, bananas, green peppers, parsnips, potatoes, spinach, eggs, calves' liver, chicken, scallops, shrimps and black pepper.

Dietary supplements can help

The WNAS has researched and formulated a special supplement

called Normoglycaemia, which is designed to normalize blood sugar levels. It contains optimum amounts of chromium and magnesium, both of which have been shown to help sugar cravings. In our experience it is ideal to take a supplement like Normoglycaemia for about four months. It acts as a 'nutritional prop', which seems to be needed initially in order to control the blood sugar levels whilst establishing new eating patterns. More information on this supplement is given on page 55.

Preparing vegetables

Fresh green vegetables supply important nutrients and should be eaten at least once daily, preferably twice. How fresh is fresh? Ideally, you should shop at least twice per week for your vegetables. Keeping them in the fridge will help keep them fresh that bit longer. Try to buy organic vegetables or grow your own in order to lessen your intake of chemicals.

The benefits your body receives from your vegetables depends greatly on how you prepare and cook them. Chopping too small or too finely will allow a greater loss of all the essential vitamins and minerals they contain. Avoid boiling them until soft. Try to change your tastes and those of your family so that you enjoy your vegetables with a little 'bite' or crunch to them. Try using less water, and use a lid on your saucepan; this helps to steam them, which is more economical too. You can also use a metal colander or steamer with a lid, over a saucepan of boiling water. No matter how carefully you cook vegetables, you are likely to lose up to 50% of the nutrients – beware! Remember that raw vegetables are very high in nutrients and fibre, so plenty of crunchy salads, please.

How to maintain blood sugar levels

Eat small regular snacks and meals. Example:

7.30 am	breakfast
10.30 am	mid-morning snack
1.00 pm	lunch

4.00 pm	mid-afternoon snack
7.00 pm	dinner
9.30 pm	light snack

For some people this may strike a chord of horror with weight gain fears. This need not be so, and in fact we usually find that women lose weight on this kind of nutritional programme. Do not forget, also, that you are cutting out the high calories in sugary foods, and replacing these with more nutritious foods.

Alternative snacks

Before unwrapping the next bar of chocolate stop and think – do you really want the symptoms of headache and fatigue that are likely to follow a few hours later, not to mention the weight gain and spotty skin that may develop? Try to choose from the following instead:

1. Unsalted nuts or seeds – one or two tablespoons should satisfy your hunger, and they are also highly nutritious.
2. Fresh fruit, particularly bananas, can satisfy your hunger.
3. Dried fruits such as raisins, apricots or La Fruit pieces which are available from health food shops.
4. Low-sugar or sugar-free fruit and nut bars.
5. Ryvita with a topping (if you are not avoiding grains). These do contain salt, so should be avoided two weeks pre-menstrually.
6. Low-fat natural or live yogurt with added seeds or fruit. If you are following a low dairy diet remember that this comes out of your dairy allowance.
7. Goat's yogurt, provided you keep within your dairy allowance.
8. Raw carrots or celery are nice and crisp to nibble on with dips such as hummus, taramasalata or guacamole.
9. Potato salad – again add chives, spring onions or chopped crisp Chinese leaves to make it more appetizing.
10. Rice cakes, either on their own or with a savoury or sweet topping such as mashed sardines or sliced bananas.

11. Rice salad, which can be cooked and made whilst you are cooking the evening meal and taken to work or kept in the fridge for use the next day. A couple of tablespoons would provide a good snack. Chop nuts, peppers, fruit, celery or any salad vegetable into it to make it more interesting.

What to avoid

Cakes, biscuits, sweet puddings, jams, jelly, ice cream, sweets, chocolate, and any packet foods such as breakfast cereals with sugar high on the ingredient list.

What to use instead

Sweeteners in drinks are not ideal. Try to dispense with your sweet tooth gradually by slowly reducing the amount of sugar added to your drinks.

Jams: sugar-free jams are available from health food shops. Try the Whole Earth variety – they are delicious.

Desserts: you will find that many of the dessert recipes in this book are in fact made without sugar, and fresh fruit salads or baked fruit make a naturally sweet alternative.

Drinks: adding hot or cold water or carbonated water to fresh fruit juice makes a refreshing drink in place of sugary fizzy drinks. These days you can buy ready-made natural alternatives such as Irish Spring, Jive, Appletize, Amé etc.

Snacks: see above for alternatives to the tea-break chocolate or biscuit.

MOOD SWINGS AND IRRITABILITY

These are problems that anyone can suffer from, perhaps when under stress, but it is the degree of suffering and frequency that make them more of a problem for PMS sufferers.

Many women find that their tolerance level is greatly reduced pre-menstrually and they frequently find themselves screaming, shouting or striking out at their husband, children or loved one for little or no reason. Sometimes an innocent comment or clumsy child can cause a severe reaction; had the same thing occurred at any other time of the month the incident would probably have gone unnoticed.

Mood swings and irritability are not just emotions that one can always control if 'one pulls oneself together'; they can often be caused by dietary factors and social poisons, especially pre-menstrually when your body is more susceptible. By simply reducing or, in a severe sufferer's case, avoiding completely the foods that may aggravate the feeling, the symptoms may greatly reduce or be eradicated altogether.

What to avoid

Tea	Impedes the absorption of important nutrients, particularly iron, which is important to menstruating women. This can aggravate heart pounding, irritability, insomnia, constipation and tremors.
Coffee	Again, it impedes absorption of important nutrients and can also cause heart pounding, irritability, insomnia, diarrhoea and tremors.
Sugar	Sugary foods can affect your blood sugar levels, causing swings from high to low. It seems that pre-menstrually some women experience typical symptoms of hypoglycaemia (low blood sugar), which include mood swings and irritability, fatigue and depression.
Alcohol	Alcohol knocks most nutrients sideways and can affect our emotional state, sometimes making us very happy, but more often hypersensitive, irritable and moody.
Smoking	Interferes with digestion, reduces vitamin C levels and causes irritability.

Try to keep all the above to a minimum, as they will only be tolerated in small amounts initially. If you have been a long-term smoker, it is probably better to get your new diet well and truly established and get your symptoms stabilized to some degree before attempting to cut down or give up smoking. The purpose of this approach is to avoid additional withdrawal symptoms occurring whilst you still have severe PMS symptoms.

What to use instead

Tea   There are many substitutes to suit all tastes – herby, fruity, flowery, decaffeinated or the tea lookalike Rooibosch 11 o'clock Tea.

Coffee   Decaffeinated coffee can be used as a substitute, but kept to a maximum of two cups per day. There are other chemicals in decaffeinated coffee besides caffeine, and these too can aggravate PMS symptoms. Try dandelion coffee, Barley Cup or chicory.

Sugar   Substitutes are not always ideal, especially as you need to train your palate to accept less sugary-tasting foods. Try to cut down generally on sugar in drinks and foods and snacks containing sugar.

Alcohol   Social situations can make avoiding alcohol difficult. However, you should try to stick to mineral waters, fruit juices and alcohol-free wine or beer for now. You do have an alcohol allowance of three units per week if you are not a severe sufferer, but it should be avoided completely pre-menstrually.

There is an extensive list of alternatives on page 96.

DEPRESSION AND CHRONIC (NON-CYCLIC) SYMPTOMS

If you feel that you experience severe depression pre-menstrually and this is your only real symptom, you should see your GP for advice and support.

Any menstruating woman or woman with ovaries is still producing hormones and is susceptible to PMS. This does not, however, mean that this is the sole cause of all her problems. We have often found that women with chronic complaints such as depression, fatigue, headaches/migraines, arthritis and even backache can find that their symptoms are worsened pre-menstrually.

If any of your symptoms do not appear to have a pattern or persist throughout the month it is important that you seek correct medical advice from your GP. There may be another cause which needs treatment.

MIGRAINE AND HEADACHES

These can be particularly disruptive, especially if they last for days. Some women have to retire to a darkened room, totally away from the family and work commitments.

Whether these are a chronic problem or cyclic, certain dietary changes can help. Severe blood sugar swings can trigger a headache/migraine. See advice on page 40.

What to avoid

Fruit　　　Oranges have been known to be a cause; the fruit and juice should be avoided.

Cheese　　Hard yellow cheeses especially.

Yeast　　　See the details of yeast foods to be avoided on page 39.

Sugar　　　This can start a headache by causing large blood sugar swings.

Chocolate　Not only will the sugar content cause headaches, but it also contains caffeine, another aggravating factor.

Stress　　　Not everyone can avoid stress in their lives, but it is important to try to recognize when you are under extra stress. You can then ensure you take better care of yourself, including relaxation techniques (see exercise on page 102).

Fluids　　　We know that the hangovers from excess alcohol can be caused by dehydration. When we lead busy lives it can be easy to forget to drink enough. Try to drink plenty of mineral water; ideally consume 2½ to 3 pints of fluid daily.

BREAST PAIN AND TENDERNESS

If you have painful or lumpy breasts cyclically or all month you should see your GP for a check. All women should really check their own breasts monthly, whilst in the bath or lying in bed. Your local Family Planning Centre or GP's surgery will be able to supply you with a leaflet on how this should be done.

Severe breast tenderness can be a very distressing symptom premenstrually. Even walking downstairs or giving the children a cuddle can cause pain and many women can't bear to be touched during this time. Different-size bras are often needed premenstrually due to the size increase and tenderness. Dietary factors again influence these symptoms and a change of diet can reduce them in two to three months.

What to avoid

Smoking	Simply stopping smoking can alleviate breast symptoms.
Tea	The chemicals in tea seem to aggravate the breast tissue.
Coffee	Again, chemicals can exacerbate breast tenderness.
Dairy	Avoid a high dairy intake, as these foods can be high in saturated fats which can aggravate many breast conditions.
Salt	Salt added to cooking or at the table can aggravate fluid retention, which would worsen breast symptoms.
Salty foods	Salt is present in many foods, especially processed convenience foods: soups, ham, bacon, tinned fish in brine, crisps and even cheese. It is necesssary to avoid as many of these foods as possible at present. You should particularly aim to avoid them in the two weeks before your period.
Sugary foods	These can cause hormonal changes, which in turn can affect the fluid balance in your body.

Alcohol	As alcohol has a chemical-like action on your body it will also affect breast tissue. Additionally it impedes the absorption of good nutrients.
Fatty foods	Saturated fats should be kept down; they are contained in foods such as red meat, mince, sausages, hard margarines, lard, dripping suet, palm and coconut oil and foods containing them. Always remove the skin or fat from any meat, preferably before cooking.

What to eat instead

As well as following the general dietary recommendations for mild, moderate or severe sufferers, essential fatty acids such as fish oils are important in helping reduce breast symptoms. Oily fish are particularly important; try to have at least two to three portions per week of fish such as herrings, mackerel, pilchards, salmon, sardines, sprats and whitebait.

Supplements

Evening Primrose oil (Efamol) and natural vitamin E are of proven benefit in easing breast tenderness. (See supplement recommendations on page 54.)

PERIOD PAIN

This can be an added torment to PMS sufferers, but we have had tremendous success in helping women overcome not only period pain but irregular and heavy periods as well. Diet, exercise and supplements all play an important role. See page 200 for details of a very helpful book, *Pain-free Periods*.

Diet

Follow your PMS diet recommendations, which have been shown also to help period pain sufferers.

Exercise

Apart from the mood-raising effect of exercise, it also improves blood circulation which keeps the body operating more efficiently. When you are experiencing period pain you may not feel like exercising vigorously so try some gentle Yoga exercises and massage your tummy several times a day.

Heat

Pelvic cramps, which are essentially muscle cramps, respond to heat and direct heat relaxes the muscles. A warm hot-water bottle will feel marvellous if you are at home or you could invest in one of the wonderful portable thermal heat packs which are now available from Nutritional Health (see page 204 for details). These little pouches tuck into your clothes directly over your tummy and radiate heat for several hours. To re-use the pouch, simply boil for 15 minutes and leave to cool for a few minutes.

Smoking

This can worsen period pain and should be avoided, especially when experiencing the pain.

Supplement

Optivite or the PMS supplement, and the diet recommendations have proven to be very helpful; sometimes an extra supplement of magnesium is also necessary. (See supplement recommendations on page 56.)

Constipation

Many PMS sufferers find that they become constipated pre-menstrually; this can worsen the period pain and should therefore be avoided. Your diet programme should offer plenty of fresh vegetables, fruit and fibre; an adequate fluid supply and the use of linseeds and perhaps extra magnesium are also important. Exercise again will help constipation.

IRON-RICH DIET

ANAEMIA

This is a condition that most women will have heard of – it simply means low iron. Up to 20% of women of child-bearing age have low iron stores. As women lose iron with their monthly menstruation, it is important to ensure that the body has an adequate supply. Heavy and long periods can both cause anaemia. You are likely to be particularly susceptible if your diet is lacking in iron-rich foods or you are consuming substances that block the uptake of iron, like tea.

Symptoms

Fatigue, sore tongue, and cracking at the corners of the mouth.

What to do

If you do suffer from heavy and/or long periods you should seek your GP's advice. He may wish to give you an iron test (serum ferritin), and if necessary prescribe a course of iron and investigate the possible causes of these problems.

Vegetarians and vegans can be particularly susceptible to anaemia due to the lack of red meat in their diets. There are, of course, diet-conscious and not so diet-conscious vegetarians (see page 91). Below is a list of foods that contain iron. Include a variety of these in your diet (avoiding for now those that are not permitted in your diet recommendations).

wheat bran	mussels	parsley
beef	scallops	spring greens
lamb	almonds	leeks
liver	brazil nuts	apricots
Bovril	coconut	bananas
egg yolk	haricot beans	blackberries

sardines	mung beans	dried figs
mackerel	kidney beans	raisins
crab	avocados	prunes
cockles	lentils	

Vitamin C in your diet will increase your absorption of iron. It would therefore be preferable to eat some fruit such as an orange after your meal, or to have a glass of orange juice with your meal.

What to avoid

Tea   Tea, if taken with a meal, blocks the absorption of two thirds of the iron you would have absorbed from the vegetables in your meal. By drinking orange juice with your meal you will increase your iron absorption.

Bran   This will again block iron absorption, and is therefore best kept fairly low if you do have a persistent iron problem.

5

SUPPLEMENTING
THE DIET

If you have moderate to severe PMS you may well need to take some nutritional supplements, at least in the short term. Having said that, at the Women's Nutritional Advisory Service we do not advise people to take random supplements – in other words, a bit of this and a bit of that. The result of uneducated purchasing in the health food shop may leave you in an even more physically unbalanced and mentally confused situation. It is definitely not recommended.

There are a number of supplements that have been scientifically tried and tested over the years – we only recommend those that have been through properly conducted clinical trials. There are some which are best for general symptoms, and others which have more specialist uses. For example, the multi-vitamin and mineral preparations like Optivite, and PMT in Australia, New Zealand and Singapore, are good for general symptoms. Natural vitamin E is particularly good for breast symptoms, as is Evening Primrose oil (Efamol), which is also effective in overcoming skin conditions. Extra vitamin C is advisable daily if you are a smoker. The supplement Normoglycaemia may be useful if you experience pre-menstrual sugar cravings.

The information on the following pages will give you some idea of the strengths of key supplements in treating certain symptoms, and the dosages required.

OPTIVITE

A multi-mineral and multi-vitamin formulation which is the most clinically tried and tested vitamin and mineral supplement in the world for PMS symptoms. It was formulated by Dr Guy Abraham, a former professor of obstetrics and gynaecology in California. It has been available for some fifteen years, and has helped many thousands of women.

Daily dosage

Two to six tablets per day. If you have severe symptoms you will need to take four tablets per day, from the first day of your period until the middle of your cycle, when you increase to six tablets per day until your period arrives. For moderate sufferers the dosage would be lower – two to four tablets per day. Mild sufferers need only take one or two tablets per day.

Availability

In the UK Optivite is available in chemists, health food shops and by mail order. For availability in Australia and New Zealand, see page 210.

EVENING PRIMROSE OIL (EFAMOL)

Evening Primrose oil has been the subject of a great deal of research. It has been shown to be extremely effective for the treatment of breast symptoms and skin conditions like eczema.

Daily dosage

Between four and eight capsules per day.

Availability

Evening Primrose oil is available on National Health Service prescription under the name of Efamast. It is also available in other countries (see page 210).

NATURAL VITAMIN E

Natural vitamin E has also been the subject of medical research. It is of proven benefit in the treatment of skin conditions and breast tenderness.

Daily dosage

The recommended daily dosage is 400 iu (international units) per day.

NORMOGLYCAEMIA

This is a special combination of vitamins and minerals that have been put together to help overcome cravings for sweet food. The formulation is based on the research of the WNAS. It contains high levels of the mineral chromium, which has been shown to help normalize blood sugar levels.

Daily dosage

One to two tablets per day, before meals, depending on severity of symptoms.

Availability

Normoglycaemia is available from Nutritional Health (for details see page 204).

MAGNESIUM

We have found this to be very helpful in dealing with period cramps. Magnesium is important to the muscles and can help reduce the cramps experienced at the time of the period.

Daily dose

Magnesium amino-acid chelate, 150 mg, two to three daily every day of your cycle.

Availability

Nutritional Health and some health food shops.

6

A SIX-MONTH INVESTMENT

THE SHORT TERM

Once you have selected the type of diet to follow, you need to stick to it as closely as possible for the first three months. If your symptoms are mild, you may not need to take nutritional supplements, as long as you keep to the diet. If, however, your symptoms are moderate to severe, you will undoubtedly need to take nutritional supplements for the first six months at least. Select your supplements from Chapter 5 and follow the recommendations carefully.

Exercise is of proven benefit, particularly for women suffering anxiety, irritability, insomnia and depression. Choose the exercises you enjoy, and work out a weekly routine for yourself. You need to exercise at least three or four times per week for at least forty minutes each time. If you can't get out to an exercise session, use one of the YMCA exercise videos at home.

You might find it useful to chart your symptoms on a daily basis. It is handy to have records to refer to, rather than relying on your memory.

THE MEDIUM TERM

After about three to four months your symptoms should be more or less under control. Once you have reached the point where you feel significantly better, you can start to adjust your diet and reduce the nutritional supplements gradually.

If you have been following a wheat-free or yeast-free diet, you can begin to reintroduce the foods you have been avoiding, one by one. Allow five to seven days between introducing new foods, so that any reactions you may have will be clearly attributable to a specific food. If you have been avoiding all grains, select one type of grain to try – wheat, for example. Include it in your diet for several days. If you do not experience any adverse reactions, wait a few days and then introduce the next grain.

If, whilst you are adding wheat to your diet, you experience 'old symptoms' again, be they fatigue, abdominal bloating, constipation, headaches or whatever, stop the wheat immediately and put it on your 'black list'. Return to your basic diet and wait a few days before trying the next type of grain, in order to avoid confusion.

Once you have experimented with the different types of food you had previously been avoiding, and have put together the diet that seems to suit your body, continue with it for another three months. Keep taking the nutritional supplements each day of your cycle, and continue with your exercise programme.

SURVIVING SYMPTOM-FREE IN THE LONG TERM

Any diet and exercise programme, even when you are feeling well, only works if you happen to like the diet and the exercises you are following. If you are not keen on either the type of diet or the exercises, it is fairly obvious that you will not have the inclination to stick to the regime in the long term. Hopefully you will be happy with your new diet and exercise regime.

In our experience, women's tastes change so much during the first few months that they have little desire to return to their previous way of eating – or drinking, for that matter. It should be said, however, that we do not expect you to turn into a 'nutritional saint' forever. Once you have the certainty about what your body likes and dislikes on a regular basis, it is perfectly acceptable for you to 'cheat' when on holiday, on a special occasion or at a dinner party. If you do experience symptoms again after one of these episodes, then all you need to do is go back on the basic diet for a week or two, until you feel completely well again. After a while you will get to know your own body and what it requires of you.

Continue with your exercise routine as regularly as you possibly can. You will find that you feel so much better. If you need further information, consult the book *Beat PMS Through Diet*, and if you need further help and guidance you can contact us at the WNAS.

LONG-TERM MANAGEMENT

Ideally, in the long term, it is preferable to manage with diet alone. However, you may feel that you would like to go on taking your supplements, perhaps on a reduced dosage, to safeguard against the return of symptoms and as an 'insurance policy' to maintain a good balance of health generally.

On long-term follow-up on WNAS patients we discovered that former PMS sufferers prefer to maintain their supplements in one of three ways:

1. To continue to take a reduced dosage of supplements every day of their menstrual cycle as an insurance.
2. To take supplements only on those days before the period when they would normally have had symptoms.
3. To take supplments only when under stress, or when travelling away from home and their normal diet.

It is really up to you to decide which long-term option you feel happiest with. You might like to start with Option 1 and work your way through to Option 3 over a few years. It is certainly felt that moderate daily dietary supplementation may well be a good idea in the long term, in view of the fact that so many nutrients are lost to the environment or in the process of cooking.

The following three chapters include sample menus for different degrees of symptoms. They need not be followed exactly on a daily basis, but will give you an idea of the range and types of foods you should be eating. Time and finances will play a part in your meal planning so you can adjust these examples to suit your requirements, as long as you keep within the guidelines of your particular diet recommendations. You will notice that some dishes are marked with an asterisk. This simply means that there is a recipe for the dish in the recipe section.

If you select a restricted diet to follow, you will need to look out for the specialized recipes. For example wheat-, oats-, barley- and rye-free recipes will be marked with a G, low-yeast recipes will be marked with a Y, and wholewheat-free recipes will be marked with a W. Vegetarian recipes can be found on page 92.

Write down your personal recommendations as you select them so you have them at hand for reference. Before selecting a dish, check the list of ingredients in the recipe section to make sure that none of them is forbidden to you.

7

RECOMMENDATIONS AND MENUS FOR MILD SUFFERERS

TEA

Reduce intake of tea to a maximum of three weak cups per day.

COFFEE

Only one cup of standard coffee and a maximum of three cups of decaffeinated coffee per day.

ALCOHOL

Keep this to a maximum of three to four drinks per week, but avoid for one week before your period.

RED MEAT

Keep to a maximum of three to four portions per week.

DAIRY

Keep your dairy consumption down to a maximum of 1 pint per day (or equivalent – see page 97).

SALT

Avoid adding salt at the table, and try to use salt substitute like LoSalt, which is a potassium-rich salt substitute, in your cooking instead. Additionally try to get used to flavouring foods with fresh herbs and spices.

VEGETABLES

Increase your consumption of greens and other fresh vegetables to at least once daily. Buy organic vegetables, or use home-grown where possible.

WHOLEFOODS

Try to ensure that your diet contains plenty of wholefoods – unprocessed grains in the form of wholemeal bread, oats, rye and so on. Use fresh foods as opposed to frozen where possible (fresh fish instead of frozen fish fingers, for example). Good-quality natural vegetable oils should also be used in cooking, and vegetable margarines instead of too much butter.

SUGAR

Keep sugar consumption low in the form of sugar added to drinks: try to reduce this gradually. Where sugary foods are concerned, let yourself have an occasional treat but not in the week before your period. Soft drinks also have a high sugar content, so reduce your consumption of these to two to three per week; again be careful in the week before your period, because of blood sugar swings (see page 40). Don't forget your regular exercise programme and your daily supplements.

For help with keeping to this regime, see Chapter 10.

FAST OPTION MENU EXAMPLES

Lunches
   Wholemeal sandwiches with fish or meat and salad
   Tuna and salad roll
   Scrambled egg and beans on toast
   Tinned mackerel with jacket potato and salad
   Avocado salad
   Home-made soup and salad
   Fresh fruit, nuts, yogurt and salad
   Toasted sandwiches
   Fish salad
   Ravioli and salad

Dinners
   Mushroom omelette and vegetables
   Steak and mushroom pie and vegetables
   Lamb chops and vegetables
   Steamed salmon with vegetables and rice
   Tuna and pasta bake (wholewheat pasta)
   Lasagne (wholewheat pasta)
   Fish pie
   Prawn and egg salad
   Pizza (wholemeal) and salad
   Wholemeal pancakes with vegetables

SAMPLE MENUS

There are two weeks' worth of sample menus. If required, please use snacks of your choice from the snack list on page 43. For dessert have fresh fruit or one of the sweets in Chapter 17. The starred items will be found in the recipe section.

WEEK 1

DAY 1

Breakfast   Dried fruit compote*

Lunch   Jacket potato
Low sugar and salt baked beans with green salad

Dinner   Roast chicken with orange and herb sauce*
Chinese leaves
Courgettes
Roast potatoes

Sweet   Rhubarb and ginger mousse*

DAY 2

Breakfast   ½ grapefruit sprinkled with nuts
1 slice wholemeal toast with sugar-free jam

Lunch   Cottage cheese and salad sandwich made with
wholemeal bread

Dinner   Grilled turkey breast
Bean and sweetcorn salad*
Lettuce with spicy lentil dressing*
Green beans

Sweet   Fresh fruit salad*

DAY 3

Breakfast   2 boiled eggs with 1 slice wholemeal toast
Live yogurt

Lunch   Grilled fillet of plaice
Grilled tomatoes
Broccoli
Mashed potatoes

Dinner   Spiced liver*
Brown rice
Spinach salad*

Sweet   Melon and ice Cream*

DAY 4

Breakfast   Cornflakes
Apple juice
1 chopped apple

Lunch   Tuna jacket*
Watercress, fennel and lemon salad*

Dinner   Piquant pork chops*
Broccoli
Carrots
Boiled potatoes

Sweet   Baked apples* stuffed with chopped nuts, raisins
and honey

DAY 5

Breakfast   Poached egg on wholemeal toast

Lunch   Salmon potato cakes*
Beansprout salad*

Dinner   Grilled chicken with mustard sauce*
Spinach
Cauliflower
Brown rice

Sweet   Apple and passion fruit delight*

DAY 6

Breakfast   Fresh fruit salad*
Yogurt

Lunch   Bean and carrot soup*
French bread with green salad

Dinner   Fish moussaka*
Cauliflower and cabbage

Sweet   Dried fruit compote* with bio yogurt

DAY 7

Breakfast   Grilled mushrooms on wholemeal toast

Lunch   Grilled plaice
Peas
Grilled tomatoes
Sauté potatoes

Dinner   Steak with mixed herbs*
Spinach salad*
Jacket potato

Sweet Orange jelly*

WEEK 2

DAY 1

Brekfast Fresh fruit salad*
    Live yogurt

Lunch Chilled tomato soup*
    Wholemeal toast

Dinner Herb-baked gammon*
    Spinach
    Sweetcorn
    Roast potatoes

Sweet Baked bananas* and ice cream

DAY 2

Breakfast Porridge made with water
    1 chopped banana
    1 tablespoon seeds or ground nuts

Lunch Cold chicken breast
    Waldorf salad*
    Cold brown rice

Dinner Plaice with yogurt and nuts*
    Carrots
    Red cabbage
    Boiled potatoes

Sweet Rice pudding

DAY 3

Breakfast	Rice Krispies 1 chopped apple Skimmed milk
Lunch	Tuna and salad sandwich made with wholemeal bread
Dinner	Lamb chops with rosemary* Cabbage and broccoli Grilled tomatoes Jacket potato
Sweet	Fruit mousse*

DAY 4

Breakfast	Scrambled egg on wholemeal toast
Lunch	Cold turkey Green salad* Brown rice
Dinner	Fisherman's pie* Peas Sweetcorn
Sweet	Banana cake*

DAY 5

Breakfast	Wholemeal toast Sugar-free jam
Lunch	Jacket potato 50 g (2 oz) grated cheese Coleslaw salad*

Dinner	Grilled chicken with tomato sauce*
	Red cabbage
	French beans
	Boiled potatoes

Sweet	Nutty carob slice*

DAY 6

Breakfast	Oats with skimmed milk
	Chopped fresh fruit
	1 tablespoon nuts

Lunch	Leek and potato soup*
	French bread

Dinner	Mackerel with lemon stuffing*
	Spinach
	Carrots
	Boiled potatoes

Sweet	Apple and tofu cheesecake*

DAY 7

Breakfast	2 boiled eggs
	1 slice wholemeal bread

Lunch	Steamed cod's roe
	Minty cabbage salad*
	Potato salad*

Dinner	Beef and bean casserole* with brown rice, broccoli and carrots
	Brown rice

Sweet	Pineapple cake*

8

RECOMMENDATIONS AND MENUS FOR MODERATE SUFFERERS

TEA

Only one or two weak cups per day.

COFFEE

Avoid standard coffee, but up to two cups of decaffeinated per day.

ALCOHOL

A maximum of one to two drinks per week, but avoid altogether for two weeks pre-menstrually.

SMOKING

Try to stop smoking altogether.

DAIRY

Keep consumption down to 1 pint total dairy allowance per day – (or equivalent – see page 97).

RED MEAT

Maximum of two to three portions per week.

FISH

Try to eat regularly, especially oily fish.

FRESH VEGETABLES

Aim to eat three portions of vegetables per day including one green leafy vegetable, like cabbage, broccoli, spinach etc., which are rich in both magnesium and iron.

SUGAR

Avoid adding sugar to drinks and eating sugary foods.

EAT SMALL REGULAR SNACKS AND MEALS

Your calorie requirements go up by approximately 500 calories per day during your pre-menstrual week. Make sure that you have a mid-morning and mid-afternoon snack at these times in addition to your meals (see page 43 for ideas).

SALT

Avoid adding salt at the table and try to use a potassium-rich salt substitute like LoSalt and get used to flavouring food with fresh herbs and spices.

FRESH FRUIT

Have at least two portions of fresh fruit each day.

WHEAT

Avoid whole wheat products (see details of sensitivities on page 36). It should not be necessary to avoid all grains unless you find that the symptoms mentioned there are persistent.

WHOLEFOODS

Eat plenty of unprocessed and natural foods.

EXERCISE

Exercise for 30–40 minutes, three times per week to the point of breathlessness. Aerobic exercise encourages the release of the brain chemicals endorphins which raise mood levels and influence hormones positively.

For help with keeping to this regime, see Chapter 10.

FAST OPTION MENU EXAMPLES

Lunches
   Sardines on white toast with salad
   French bread filled with fish, meat or cheese and salad
   Eggs and beans on toast
   Danish open sandwiches on pumpernickel
   White bread sandwiches with salad
   Jacket potato with tuna and sweetcorn filling and salad
   Quiche with salad

Macaroni cheese
Mixed cheese and salad platter with Ryvita
Hummus with raw vegetable crudités and pitta bread

Dinners
Mixed vegetable crumble
Tortellini with salad
Cauliflower cheese with jacket potato
Quorn pie (white flour) with a selection of vegetables
Steak and mushroom pie with broccoli, carrots and potatoes
Pizza (white flour) and salad
Tuna and pasta bake (white pasta)
Turkey snitzel with vegetables
Cold meat or fish salad
Fish in breadcrumbs with vegetables

SAMPLE MENUS

Here is a week's worth of sample menus. The starred items will be found in the recipe section. Please use snacks of your choice from p. 43. You can substitute the dessert with fresh fruit.

DAY 1

Breakfast	2 scrambled eggs on white toast
	1 yogurt
Lunch	Smoked mackerel
	Minty cabbage salad*
	Brown rice
Dinner	Roast chicken
	Broccoli
	Carrots
	Jacket or boiled potatoes
Sweet	Fresh fruit salad*

DAY 2

Breakfast	Rice Krispies with skimmed milk Chopped banana and 1 tablespoon linseeds
Lunch	Pizza toast* Watercress, fennel and lemon salad*
Dinner	Almond trout* Brown rice Spinach Sweetcorn
Sweet	Apple and tofu cheesecake*

DAY 3

Breakfast	3 grilled tomatoes on white toast
Lunch	Grilled sardines Jacket potato Green salad*
Dinner	Gammon steak Orange sauce* Brown rice Carrots Broccoli
Sweet	Baked apple* stuffed with chopped nuts, raisins and honey

DAY 4

Breakfast   Porridge (made with half water and half milk)
             1 chopped banana

Lunch   Nutty sprout stir-fry*
             Brown rice

Dinner   Broccoli and sweetcorn plaice*
             Carrots
             Cabbage
             Jacket or boiled potatoes

Sweet   Orange jelly*

DAY 5

Breakfast   2 slices white toast with sugar-free marmalade

Lunch   Spinach gratin*
             Baked potato

Dinner   Grilled lamb chop
             Gravy
             Courgettes
             Green beans
             Jacket or boiled potatoes

Sweet   Banana and tofu cream*

DAY 6

Breakfast   Fresh fruit salad*
             1 tablespoon raisins and mixed nuts
             1 yogurt

Lunch   Brown lentil soup*
             2 Ryvitas

Dinner	Halibut fruit*
	Spinach
	Brown rice
Sweet	Slice of pineapple cake*

DAY 7

Breakfast	2 boiled eggs
	1–2 slices white bread
Lunch	Tuna jacket potato*
Dinner	Grilled lean steak
	Baked nutty onions*
	Broccoli
	Grilled tomatoes
	Baked or boiled potatoes
Sweet	Piece of fresh fruit

WEEK 2

DAY 1

Breakfast	Yogurt with 1 tablespoon linseeds
	1 chopped banana
Lunch	Mushroom with mint soup*
	1 slice of white toast
Dinner	Chicken with almonds*
	Leeks
	Broccoli
	Brown rice
Sweet	Dried fruit compote* and bio yogurt

DAY 2

Breakfast	Cornflakes with skimmed milk 1 chopped apple 1 tablespoon raisins
Lunch	Cooked mussels with lemon juice and black pepper Brown rice salad*
Dinner	Lamb and parsley stew* Carrots Spring greens Mashed potatoes
Sweet	Baked apple* stuffed with chopped nuts, raisins and honey

DAY 3

Breakfast	1 scrambled egg 1 slice of white toast 2 grilled tomatoes
Lunch	Jacket potato 50 g (2 oz) grated cheese Coleslaw salad*
Dinner	Grilled mackerel Sweetcorn Broccoli Sauté potatoes
Sweet	Rhubarb and ginger mousse*

DAY 4

Breakfast	Fresh fruit salad* 1 tablespoon linseeds 1 tablespoon mixed nuts
Lunch	Fish soup* 2 rice cakes or 1 slice of white toast
Dinner	Steak and bananas* Grilled mushrooms Spinach Jacket potato
Sweet	Apple custard*

DAY 5

Breakfast	Rice Krispies with skimmed milk 1 chopped orange
Lunch	Grilled plaice Tomato sauce* Spinach salad*
Dinner	Sussex casserole* Brown rice
Sweet	Melon ice cream*

DAY 6

Breakfast	2 boiled eggs 2 rice cakes with sugar-free jam
Lunch	Cottage cheese Beetroot and cabbage salad* Potato salad*

Dinner	Prawn provençale*
	Brown rice
Sweet	Apple and passion fruit delight*

DAY 7

Breakfast	3 grilled tomatoes on white toast
	1 yogurt
Lunch	Jacket potato
	2 grilled sardines
	Bean and sweetcorn salad*
Dinner	Turkey breast with mushroom sauce*
	Spinach
	Leeks
	Sauté potatoes
Sweet	Orange jelly*

9

RECOMMENDATIONS AND MENUS FOR SEVERE SUFFERERS

TEA

Restrict to only one weak cup per day or better still, use Rooibosch 11 o'clock Tea instead.

COFFEE

Should be avoided altogether initially. Restrict to a maximum of two cups of decaffeinated coffee per day. Preferably substitute altogether (see list of alternative drinks on p. 96).

COLA-BASED DRINKS

Should be avoided altogether.

ALCOHOL

Should be avoided altogether initially.

SMOKING

Try to cut down gradually. It is better to try to reduce your cigarette consumption after your period rather than during your pre-menstrual phase.

DAIRY

Keep total dairy consumption down to less than 1 pint per day (see page 97).

RED MEAT

Restrict to a maximum of two portions per week, preferably organic or additive-free.

FISH

Try to eat four to five portions per week, especially oily fish, e.g. herring, mackerel, sardines or salmon when in season.

VEGETABLES

Aim to eat three portions of vegetables per day, including one green leafy vegetable such as cabbage, broccoli, spinach etc., which are rich in both magnesium and iron.

SALAD

Aim to eat a salad each day.

SUGAR

Avoid white or brown sugar and sugary foods.

SALT

Avoid adding salt at the table and try to use a potassium-rich salt substitute like LoSalt and get used to flavouring food with fresh herbs and spices.

SALTY FOODS

Avoid eating foods with a high salt content as salt drags fluid into the cells.

FRESH FRUIT

Aim to have at least three portions daily.

GRAINS

Avoid all wheat, barley, oats, rye and corn (see page 36).

OILS

Use good-quality polyunsaturated vegetable oils, like sunflower or safflower oils, but try to keep consumption fairly low.

WHOLEFOODS

Eat plenty of unprocessed and natural foods.

ADDITIVES

Avoid altogether or greatly restrict additives pre-menstrually (see list p. 101).

EXERCISE

Exercise for 30–40 minutes, three times per week to the point of breathlessness. Aerobic exercise encourages the release of the brain chemicals endorphins which raise mood levels and influence hormones positively.

OTHER USEFUL ADVICE

1. Eat regular snacks and meals.
2. Plan meals ahead, preferably before you go shopping.
3. Don't go shopping on an empty stomach.

For help with keeping to this regimen, see Chapter 10.

FAST OPTION MENU EXAMPLES

Lunches
  Mackerel and salad with rice cakes
  Cheese omelette and salad
  Greek salad
  Jacket potato with filling
  Prawn and rice salad
  Rice salad with nuts
  Yogurt with nuts, seeds and fresh fruit
  Turkey salad
  Vegetable soup and salad
  Hummus, guacamole or taramasalata with raw vegetables, crudités and corn wafers.

Dinners
  Steamed salmon with vegetables and rice
  Lamb chops with a selection of vegetables
  Mixed vegetables with almond stir-fry and rice noodles
  Grilled fish with boiled potatoes, broccoli and carrots

Corn tacos with mince or beans, sour cream, guacamole and salsa and salad

Prawn and egg salad

Steak vegetables and salad

Cauliflower cheese (using corn flour) and jacket potato

Spaghetti Bolognese sauce with rice noodles or corn pasta

Cold meat or fish salad

SAMPLE MENUS

Here are two weeks' worth of sample menus, followed by some vegetarian menus. Please note, white flour can be replaced with rice, potato flour, dal or cornflour or a combination.

WEEK 1

DAY 1

Breakfast   Cornflakes
Skimmed milk or apple juice
1 chopped apple
1 tablespoon linseeds

Snack   50–75g (2–3 oz) unsalted nuts or seeds

Lunch   Jacket potato
Sardines
Green salad*

Snack   1 banana

Dinner	Grilled lamb chop with tomato sauce*
	Carrots
	Fresh greens
	Potatoes
Sweet	Orange jelly*

DAY 2

Breakfast	2–3 rice cakes
	Sugar-free jam
	Fresh fruit salad*
Snack	1 natural yogurt with 1 tablespoon linseeds
Lunch	Chicken and spinach soup*
	French bread
Snack	50–75 g (2–3 oz) raw carrot
Dinner	Dutch pork*
	Green salad*
	Brown rice*
Sweet	Apple custard*

DAY 3

Breakfast	2 boiled eggs
	2 rice cakes
	1 apple
Snack	50–75 g (2–3 oz) unsalted mixed nuts
Lunch	Lean ham
	Jacket potato
	Coleslaw salad*
Snack	1 banana

Dinner   Haddock Florentine*
            Brown rice
            Fresh broccoli
            Sweetcorn

Sweet   Apple and passion fruit delight*

DAY 4

Breakfast   Cornflakes
            Skimmed milk
            1 banana
            1 tablespoon linseeds

Snack   1 apple

Lunch   Grilled plaice with mustard sauce*
            Boiled potatoes
            Greens
            Cauliflower

Snack   1 orange

Dinner   Haddock kedgeree*
            Watercress, fennel and lemon salad*

Sweet   Rhubarb and ginger mousse*

DAY 5

Breakfast   Yogurt with chopped apple
            1 tablespoon linseeds

Snack   2 rice cakes with sugar-free peanut butter

Lunch   Grilled chicken, hot or cold
            Potato salad*
            Beetroot cabbage salad*

Snack   50–75g (2–3 oz) unsalted seeds

Dinner	Vegetable curry*
	Brown rice
Sweet	Fresh fruit salad*

DAY 6

Breakfast	Rice Krispies
	Skimmed milk
	1 banana
	1 tablespoon linseeds
Snack	1 apple
Lunch	Brown lentil soup*
	2 rice cakes
Snack	50–75g (2–3 oz) unsalted mixed nuts
Dinner	Liver and sweetcorn casserole*
	Cabbage
	Grilled mushrooms
	Baked or boiled potatoes
Sweet	Baked apple*

DAY 7

Breakfast	Grilled tomatoes
	2 egg omelette
	Grilled mushrooms
	2 rice cakes
Snack	1 banana
Lunch	Sardines
	Spinach salad*
	Rice salad*

Snack	2 rice cakes with sugar-free jam
Dinner	Hot fruity chicken*
	Carrots
	Spinach
	Jacket potato
Sweet	Fruit mousse*

For the following menus, please add mid-morning, mid-afternoon and mid-evening snacks of your choice from the list on page 43. Fresh fruit or a suitable sweet from the recipe section can be eaten after the main course at dinner.

WEEK 2

Some white flour has been included in this week for those that find it too difficult to avoid grains altogether.

DAY 1

Breakfast	Oats, soaked overnight with skimmed milk
	Yogurt and chopped banana
	1 tablespoon linseeds
Lunch	Pilchards on white toast
	Beansprout salad*
Dinner	Roast turkey
	Parsley and lemon stuffing*
	Parsnips
	Cabbage
	Roast potatoes
Sweet	Baked banana*

DAY 2

Breakfast   1 slice white toast
             Scrambled egg

Lunch   Jacket potato with tuna
             Salad of your choice*

Dinner   Steak and bananas*
             Green beans
             Red cabbage
             Sauté potatoes

Sweet   Orange jelly*

DAY 3

Breakfast   Cornflakes
             Skimmed milk
             Chopped apple
             1 tablespoon linseeds

Lunch   Spinach and avocado salad*
             Brown rice

Dinner   Fish pudding*
             Broccoli
             Grilled tomatoes

Sweet   Rice pudding

DAY 4

Breakfast   2 Ryvita with sugar-free jam
             1 yogurt with chopped banana
             1 tablespoon linseeds

Lunch   Tomato and black pepper omelette

	Salad of your choice*
Dinner	Red mullet in tomato sauce*
	Green beans
	Sweetcorn
	Boiled potatoes
Sweet	Fresh fruit salad*

DAY 5

Breakfast	Fresh fruit salad*
	1 tablespoon nuts
Lunch	Mushroom and mint soup*
	1 slice white toast
Dinner	Spiced lentil cakes*
	Minty cabbage salad*
Sweet	Banana and tofu cream*

DAY 6

Breakfast	Poached egg on white toast
	Grilled tomatoes
Lunch	Jacket potato
	Baked beans (low salt and sugar)
	50 g (2 oz) grated cheese
Dinner	Liver kebabs*
	Salad of your choice*
	Brown rice
Sweet	Dried fruit compote*

DAY 7

Breakfast   Oats soaked overnight with chopped fruit
Skimmed milk
1 tablespoon linseeds

Lunch   Bean and carrot soup*
French bread

Dinner   Pork chops with tomato and mushrooms*
Spinach
Carrots
Boiled potatoes

Sweet   Rhubarb and ginger mousse*

SAMPLE DRINKS

Herbal teas	unlimited
2 cups decaffeinated coffee	maximum
½ glass apple juice/ orange juice diluted with water	unlimited
Mineral waters	unlimited

RECOMMENDATIONS FOR VEGETARIANS AND VEGANS

Vegetarians need to be sure to include a variety of vegetable proteins in their diet as no one vegetable protein contains all the required nutrients. Vegetarian proteins include: nuts, seeds, peas, beans, lentils, wholegrain, brown rice, sprouted beans, soya bean and Quorn products.

Many vegetarians do take good care over their diet but there are some who replace the meat and fish with too much cheese and junk foods. The menus and recipes on page 92 should help you to follow your PMS diet recommendations. They have been designed for vegetarians who are moderate to severe PMS sufferers. If you suffer mild to moderate PMS symptoms, and usually follow a vegetarian diet, you can use the menus as a guideline, and add in wholegrain products, like wholewheat bread, pasta and pastry.

There are also vegans who look after their diets and vegans who do not. It is important to obtain a good specialized vegan recipe book to help you to follow your PMS diet recommendations. You should find that the vegetarian menus will be quite easy to follow with adjustments to meet your vegan regimen.

SAMPLE VEGETARIAN MENUS

Please add mid-morning, mid-afternoon and mid-evening snacks of your choice from the lists on page 43. For dessert, please have fresh fruit or select a suitable sweet from sweets in Chapter 17.

DAY 1

Breakfast	Rice Krispies
	Apple juice
	1 tablespoon linseeds

| Lunch | Tofu with minty cabbage salad* |
| | Spicy lentil dressing* |

Dinner	Nutty sprout stir-fry*
	Brown rice
	Calabrese and carrots

DAY 2

Breakfast	Live yogurt with chopped banana
	1 tablespoon linseeds
	2 rice cakes with sugar-free jam

Lunch	Jacket potato with 50 g (2 oz) cheese Salad of your choice*
Dinner	Nut and vegetable loaf* Watercress, fennel and lemon salad* Courgettes and french beans

DAY 3

Breakfast	2 boiled eggs 1 slice white toast
Lunch	Selection of mixed vegetables and brown rice stir-fried with 2 tablespoons mixed nuts or beans
Dinner	Spinach gratin* Jacket potato Carrots and parsnips

DAY 4

Breakfast	Rice Krispies Skimmed milk 2 rice cakes with sugar-free jam
Lunch	Brown lentil soup* French bread Salad of your choice*
Dinner	Mexican stuffed eggs* using almond halves Cauliflower, French beans and braised fennel

DAY 5

Breakfast	Fresh fruit salad* Yogurt

Lunch	Chickpea dips* 1 slice white toast
Dinner	Jacket potato Baked nutty onions* Spinach Celery and white cabbage

DAY 6

Breakfast	Cornflakes with chopped apple and orange Skimmed milk
Lunch	Jacket potato Cottage cheese Salad of your choice*
Dinner	Bean and carrot soup* Vegetable and dal jackets* Leeks and broccoli

DAY 7

Breakfast	Grilled tomatoes with white toast
Lunch	Potato and herb omelette* Beetroot and cabbage salad*
Dinner	Egg and vegetable bake* Brown rice Sweetcorn and carrots

10

HOW TO FOLLOW
THE DIET
RECOMMENDATIONS

This advice, with appropriate adaptations, is also relevant to women who suffer only mild or moderate symptoms.

TEA

There is one thing to remember when trying herb teas – they will not taste like or replace the need for ordinary tea. Many women find that they are addicted to tea without realizing it until they try to stop. Do bear this in mind when you have your first sip of a herbal or alternative tea and find you do not feel the same satisfaction.

There are many different teas to choose from, which can be bought in one-cup packets to save purchasing a whole box and realizing that, after one cup, it's not the tea for you. Start off making the tea weak and build up the strength as your taste buds adjust. Below are some of the popular ones you might like to try. Experiment with these teas until you find a few that you feel happy to consume on a regular basis.

It is worth noting that Rooibosch 11 o'clock Tea, which is a tea lookalike, also contains a mild antispasmodic which may help to ease muscle tensions. It has been successfully used in trials on babies with colic.

Fruity	Herb	Similar to ordinary tea
Apple and fruit	Fennel	Rooibosch 11 o'clock Tea
Orange	Camomile	Decaffeinated tea
Orchard Surprise	Nettle	Luakka
Kiwi and passion fruit	Matle	Red bush
Tropical Secret	Peppermint	
Sunburst C		
Cranberry Cove		
Rosehip		
Bramble		
Wild forest blackberry		
Raspberry Patch		

COFFEE

The same applies here as with tea – it is very difficult to get the same satisfaction initially. Do try some alternatives such as dandelion coffee (instant, which is very sweet, or dandelion root filtered through a coffee machine which makes a stronger, malted drink), chicory or Barley Cup.

DECAFFEINATED COFFEE

Caffeine has been well researched and is known to cause symptoms. Although caffeine has been removed from decaffeinated coffee it still contains other chemicals, the effects of which are not fully known. Use the suggested alternatives for tea or coffee once you have used your decaffeinated allowance for the day.

COLA

Cola drinks contain sugar and caffeine. These should be avoided. It is best to avoid even the diet and low-caffeine alternatives for now. Try fresh fruit juice with carbonated water or one of the many fruit and carbonated water drinks which are available in restaurants and bars.

ALCOHOL

This is not always very easy to avoid on special occasions or at times of celebration. But nowadays you are no longer considered a party pooper if you do not indulge in an alcoholic beverage – there are now more non-alcoholic or low-alcoholic drinks available than ever. More and more people also cater for the drivers and teetotallers in their gatherings. When out, mineral waters such as Perrier and also fruit juice and carbonated water mixes are freely available. The low-alcohol wines and beers should only be drunk once or twice per week.

SMOKING

We all know that smoking is bad for our health, but it can also worsen some PMS symptoms and reduce certain vitamin levels, particularly vitamin C. This new diet plan should inspire you to cut down drastically and eventually stop. You may need to stabilize your symptoms and adjust to the diet plan before cutting down too drastically.

DAIRY

Keep your total dairy consumption down to the equivalent of 1 pint of milk per day. This means that you can have 600 ml (1 pint) of dairy products per day (50 g (2 oz) of cheese is equivalent to 100 g (4 oz) of milk). Excessive consumption of dairy products can make PMS far worse particularly PMS A symptoms, and may interfere with the uptake of magnesium which is an important mineral for PMS sufferers. Other calcium-rich foods are almonds, brazil nuts, watercress, figs, broccoli and parsley.

MEAT/POULTRY

Keep your red meat consumption down to a maximum of two or three portions per week, and always try to eat lean meats; remove all visible fat before cooking, and remove any skin from poultry. Try to buy additive-free or, better still, organic meat where possible. Pork pies, sausages and mixed meat pies should be avoided for now. Poultry is definitely preferable to too much red meat.

FISH

Natural fish oils contain important essential fatty acids known as Eicosapentonoic Acid (EPA). Essential fatty acids are important for many body mechanisms, especially in producing hormone-like substances called prostaglandins, which help to balance sex hormones.

It is a myth that fish is fiddly to prepare. A shortage of ideas for making it more exciting seems to be a major reason for women not eating fish more regularly. It can be so quick and easy to prepare – just look at some of the recipes included in that section. Try to eat 4–5 portions of oily fish a week, e.g. herring, mackerel, salmon, pilchards or sardines.

VEGETABLES AND SALAD

Aim to eat three portions of fresh vegetables per day, including one green leafy vegetable, such as cabbage, broccoli, spinach etc., which are rich in both magnesium and iron. How fresh is fresh?

Ideally, you should shop at least twice per week for your vegetables. Keeping them in the fridge will help keep them fresh that bit longer. Try to buy organic vegetables or grow your own in order to lessen your intake of chemicals.

The benefits your body receives from your vegetables depends greatly on how you prepare and cook them. Chopping too small or too finely will allow a greater loss of all the essential vitamins and minerals they contain. Avoid boiling them until soft. Try to change your tastes and those of your family so that you enjoy your vegetables with a little 'bite' or crunch to them. Try using less water, and use a lid on your saucepan; this helps to steam them, which is more economical too. You can also use a metal colander or steamer with a lid, over a saucepan of boiling water. No matter how carefully you cook vegetables you are likely to lose up to 50% of the nutrients – beware! Remember that raw vegetables are very high in nutrients and fibre, so plenty of crunchy salads, please.

SUGAR

Blood sugar levels can be quite a problem for severe sufferers. Avoiding the refined sugars can in fact help your body to correct this problem. You will see from the recipes that sugar is not necessarily needed in 'sweets'. See page 40 for help on sugar craving and a list of alternatives to use.

REGULAR SNACKS AND MEALS

Eating wholesome food regularly helps to maintain energy and blood sugar levels, helping to reduce PMS C symptoms, mood swings, irritability and depression. It is especially important to ensure that you are eating little and often in your pre-menstrual week, as your calorie requirements go up by as much as 500 calories per day. If you are not eating high calorie food like chocolate or biscuits you need to eat quite a bit extra. See page 43 for snacks and eating pattern ideas.

SALT

It can be difficult to stop adding salt when you are cooking for the family. Try to reduce this over a week, and swap to adding a small amount of LoSalt, a potassium-rich salt substitute, instead. It is a good idea not put any salt on the table, so it cannot be added to the plate. Using spices, herbs and freshly ground black pepper can reduce the want for the salty taste. Black pepper is also rich in the mineral chromium which helps to normalize blood sugar levels.

SALTY FOODS

Watch out for the 80% of salt in our diet which is hidden in pre-packed ham, bacon, processed foods, crisps, salted nuts, fish tinned in brine and so on. Consumption of these foods should be kept low but avoided altogether in the two weeks before your period as they contain so much salt.

FRESH FRUIT

Try to eat at least three portions of fruit per day. Keep a fresh supply at home and even at work to use as a snack.

GRAINS AND WHOLEWHEAT

Avoiding grains and wholewheat can be a difficult task. It is important to ensure that these are well substituted in your diet. See pages 37–8 for alternatives and information on how to reintroduce these to your diet.

OILS

Always use good-quality vegetable oils for cooking, such as sunflower and safflower seed oils. Cold-pressed oils, such as walnut, sesame and olive oil, are also a good source of unsaturated oil for salad dressings.

WHOLEFOODS

Wholefoods mean foods that have not been processed or refined. The term also refers to grains such as wholewheat, barley, millet, rye and oats, which are fine to eat once it is established that there is no sensitivity (see page 37).

ADDITIVES

Severe PMS sufferers seem to be more sensitive before their period, and therefore more likely to react to certain additives. If you suffer badly it would be best to try and keep the additives below at a very low level in the two weeks before your period.

Azo-dyes E102, E104, E107, E110, E122, E123, E124, E128, E131, E132, E133, E142, E151, E154, E155, E180.
Benzoates E210–E219
Sulphur dioxide and sulphites E220–E227
Nitrites and nitrates E249–E252
Proprionic acid and propionates E280–E283
Anti-oxidants BHA and BHT, E320 and E321
Monosodium glutamate (MSG) and related compounds E621–E623

PLANNING

When on a restricted diet, planning is all-important. Start not with a negative list of what you cannot have, but with a list of foods that you like that you can have. Try to draw up a rough plan of your meals for the week ahead and for any packed lunches.

This will ensure that you have to hand all you need to follow your PMS diet recommendations.

It is usually not possible to cook lunches or follow the sample menus when working full-time, part-time or even just leading a very busy life. This is where planning is very important. If you have access to a work canteen you may be lucky enough to find lunches such as salads, jacket potatoes or chicken and vegetable dishes. Unfortunately this will not always be the case, so home-prepared lunches may be needed at first, especially if following the recommendations for sufferers of severe PMS symptoms.

When preparing your evening meal, give a thought to tomorrow's lunch. You can boil some brown rice and leave it to cool whilst you are cooking. Make an extra portion of salad to be left in the fridge ready to be put into a lunch box in the morning. Here are some suggestions for portable lunches: sardines, tuna, cold chicken, hard-boiled eggs, cold ham, lean beef, prawns, pilchards, tinned salmon, or any cold lean meats can be used with any combination of salads (see Chapter 11).

EXERCISE

Try 30–40 minutes' exercise three or four times a week, or daily if possible. Any exercise that stimulates the circulation would be great – swimming, squash, cycling, tennis, jogging, aerobics or even a brisk walk.

If you are not used to exercising, start slowly. Join a class or local club – it sometimes helps to make it a social arrangement, so take a friend along. Exercising at home with a video can be ideal for those with young children, who may like to join in. The YMCA make an excellent range of exercise videos starting with a low-impact, 12-minute session. Look out for their videos or contact them directly.

Research has shown that regular exercise can be of proven benefit to PMS sufferers. It not only helps to reduce fluid retention but can have a positive effect on endorphin levels. It is difficult to believe that this can help when you are feeling low and exhausted, but exercising regularly can in fact improve fatigue and is a great outlet for irritability and aggressive feelings.

It is now known that exercise will help to keep your bones strong and healthy, which is a sure way to prevent bone thinning and help to reduce the risk of osteoporosis.

PART III

THE RECIPES

11

SALADS AND DRESSINGS

Unless organically grown, fruit and vegetables are often sprayed with chemicals. It is, therefore, important that all ingredients are washed well, especially as salads are eaten raw.

Chicken and Pasta Salad G & W

Serves 4

150 g (5 oz) chicken breast fillet
225 g (8 oz) fettuccine
2 teaspoons sesame seeds
100 g (4 oz) mange-tout
100 g (4 oz) broccoli, cut into florets
1 medium green pepper, cored, seeded and sliced
6 green shallots, chopped

Dressing
30 ml (2 tablespoons) lemon juice
15 ml (1 tablespoon) French mustard
1 tablespoon chopped fresh parsley
2 teaspoons grated fresh ginger
30 ml (2 tablespoons) water

1. Poach, steam or microwave the chicken until tender. Drain, cool and slice finely.
2. Add the fettuccine to a large saucepan of boiling water. Boil rapidly, uncovered, for about 10 minutes or until just tender,

and drain. Rinse under cold water and drain again.

3. Toast the sesame seeds on an oven tray in a moderate oven and leave to cool.

4. Drop the mange-tout and broccoli into a saucepan of boiling water, return to the boil, drain, place into a bowl of iced water and drain.

5. To make the dressing, combine all the ingredients in a screw-top jar and shake well.

6. Place the fettuccine on to a serving plate, top with the mange-tout, broccoli, pepper, shallots and chicken, and sprinkle with sesame seeds. Add the dressing just before serving.

Waldorf Salad G W & Y

Serves 4

50 g (2 oz) walnuts
1 head curly endive
2 dessert apples
2 sticks celery
1 tablespoon linseeds

Chop the walnuts, endives, apples and celery, add the linseeds, and mix together.

Minty Cabbage Salad G W & Y

Serves 4

250 g (9 oz) cabbage
1 medium carrot
1 medium green pepper, cored and seeded
1 medium red pepper, cored and seeded

Shred the cabbage, grate the carrot, chop the peppers and mix all the ingredients together.

Watercress, Fennel and Lemon Salad G W & Y

Serves 4

1 large fennel bulb, thinly sliced
1 small bunch watercress, washed and trimmed
1 handful parsley, washed, well dried and finely chopped
freshly ground black pepper
1 tablespoon lemon juice (fresh)
lemon

1. Mix together the fennel, watercress and parsley.
2. Add the black pepper and lemon juice.
3. Thinly slice the lemon, cut each slice into segments and add to the salad.

Spinach and Avocado Salad G & W

Serves 4

40 English spinach leaves
200 g (7 oz) avocado, sliced
12 black olives, stoned and quartered

Dressing
10 ml (2 teaspoons) olive oil
15 ml (1 tablespoon) lemon juice (fresh)
1 garlic clove, crushed

1. Remove the thick stalks from the spinach leaves and slice the leaves into bite-size pieces.
2. Combine the spinach, avocado and olives in bowl.
3. Combine the oil, lemon juice and garlic and pour this dressing over the salad.

Beetroot and Cabbage Salad G W & Y

Serves 4

175 g (6 oz) firm white cabbage, shredded
175 g (6 oz) red cabbage, grated
175 g (6 oz) carrots, grated
1 small onion, finely chopped
½ red pepper, cored, seeded and chopped
25 g (1 oz) sunflower seeds
175 g (6 oz) raw beetroot, grated

Mix all the ingredients, leaving the beetroot until just before serving.

Spinach Salad G W & Y

Serves 4

100 g (4 oz) courgettes, thinly sliced
75 g (3 oz) carrots, grated
75 g (3 oz) baby turnips, grated
50 g (2 oz) spinach leaves, coarsely chopped
225 g (8 oz) broad beans

Mix all the ingredients together with black pepper and dressing of choice to taste.

Coleslaw G & W

Serves 4

450 g (1 lb) white cabbage, shredded
100 g (4 oz) carrots, grated
1 onion, sliced

2 tablespoons slimmers' mayonnaise *or* dressing *or* slimmers'
  natural yogurt
1 tablespoon finely chopped fresh parsley

Mix all the ingredients together, using the parsley to decorate.

Beansprout Salad W & Y

As a side salad serves 4

175 g (6 oz) beansprouts
100 g (4 oz) red pepper, cored, seeded and sliced
100 g (4 oz) can of sweetcorn, drained
2 dessert apples, grated
4 spring onions, chopped

Mix all the ingredients together with black pepper and dressing to
taste.

Bean and Sweetcorn Salad W & Y

As a side salad serves 4

225 g (8 oz) French beans, cut into 2.5 cm/1 inch lengths
100 g (4 oz) can of sweetcorn, drained
2 small spring onions, sliced
a few sesame seeds

Cook the beans for 5 minutes, drain and cool under cold water.
Drain well, and add the sweetcorn and spring onions with a
sprinkle of sesame seeds.

Green Salad G W & Y

Serves 1

50 g (2 oz) lettuce, chopped
8 slices thinly cut cucumber
½ green pepper, cored, seeded and sliced
50 g (2 oz) watercress

Mix all the ingredients together with black pepper and dressing to taste.

Brown Rice Salad W & Y

Serves 2

100 g (4 oz) cooked brown rice
75 g (3 oz) canned sweetcorn
½ red pepper, cored, seeded and sliced
½ green pepper, cored, seeded and sliced

Mix all the ingredients together with black pepper and dressing to taste.

Potato Salad G & W

Serves 2

225 g (8 oz) boiled potatoes
2 spring onions
2 tablespoons low-calorie dressing
2 tablespoons snipped fresh chives

Chop the potatoes into bite-size pieces. Chop the spring onions. Mix all the ingredients together.

Bean Salad G W & Y

As a side salad serves 4

100 g (4 oz) haricot beans, soaked overnight
100 g (4 oz) chickpeas, soaked overnight
1 bay leaf
2 sprigs of thyme
1 garlic clove, crushed
30 ml (2 tablespoons) cold-pressed olive oil *or* vegetable oil
100 g (4 oz) tinned red kidney beans
100 g (4 oz) broad beans
2 teaspoons finely chopped parsley
½ teaspoon cumin ground seeds
1 medium onion, finely chopped

1. Drain the haricot beans and chickpeas, and cover with water in a saucepan. Boil for 10 minutes, add the bay leaf and sprigs of thyme, and simmer for 1–1½ hours. Drain and leave to cool.
2. Mix the garlic with the oil and the kidney and broad beans. Pour this over the remaining beans.
3. Add the parsley, cumin seeds and onion.

Tomato Dressing/Sauce G W & Y

Serves 4 (2 tablespoons each)

10 ml (2 teaspoons) olive oil
100 g (4 oz) onion, finely chopped
1 garlic clove, crushed
400 g (14 oz) fresh ripe tomatoes chopped and skin removed,
    or 14 oz (400 ml) can plum tomatoes, drained and chopped
½ teaspoon mixed herbs *or* basil
freshly ground black pepper to taste

1. Heat the oil, adding the onion and garlic. Cover and cook gently for 5 minutes until the onion is soft.
2. Add the tomatoes and herbs. Cover and cook for 15 minutes.
3. Season with black pepper and cool (if used for salad dressing).

Spicy Lentil Dressing G W & Y

Serves 4

225 g (8 oz) red lentils
600 ml (1 pint) water
10 ml (2 teaspoons) sunflower oil
1 onion, finely chopped
1 garlic clove, crushed
½ teaspoon ginger (ground *or* grated root)
½ teaspoon ground coriander
½ teaspoon ground cumin seeds

1. Place the lentils in a saucepan and cover with the measured water.
2. Bring to the boil and simmer for 20–30 minutes until the water has been absorbed and the lentils are swollen. The lentils should look like a thickish purée.
3. Heat the oil and gently fry the onions, garlic and ginger until lightly brown, for 4–6 minutes.
4. Add the spices and cook further for 1–2 minutes.
5. Add the lentils and cook very gently for 4–5 minutes. Serve hot with rice, or cold with salad.

Orange and Herb Sauce W

Serves 4

10 ml (2 teaspoons) sunflower oil
1 small onion, finely chopped
175 ml (6 fl oz) fresh orange juice
2 teaspoons chopped tarragon
2 teaspoons chopped parsley
freshly ground black pepper
2 teaspoons cornflour
15 ml (1 tablespoon) water
1 orange, peeled, segmented, pith removed and chopped

1. Heat oil and gently fry the onion. Add the orange juice, herbs and black pepper to taste.
2. Bring to the boil and simmer for 2–3 minutes.
3. Mix the cornflour with the water and stir into the sauce, bringing slowly to the boil and stirring constantly.
4. Add the chopped orange segments, heat for 1–2 minutes and serve.

This sauce can be used to complement meat, fish or vegetable dishes, and can be made in larger quantities in advance and frozen.

12

SOUPS

Mushroom and Mint Soup W

Serves 4

4 large potatoes, peeled and coarsely chopped
1 small onion, chopped
900 ml (1½ pints) chicken stock
grated rind *and* juice of 1 lemon
1 tablespoon chopped fresh rosemary
freshly ground black pepper to taste
50 g (2 oz) margarine
225 g (8 oz) mushrooms, sliced
1 tablespoon flour
2 tablespoons finely chopped fresh mint
150 ml (5 fl oz) milk

1. Place the potatoes and onion in a large saucepan and add the stock, lemon rind, juice, rosemary and pepper.
2. Bring the mixture to the boil. Reduce the heat and simmer, stirring occasionally, for 25 minutes or until the vegetables are tender.
3. In a small saucepan, melt the margarine over a low heat. Add the mushrooms and toss them in the margarine until they are thoroughly coated. Cook them slowly, stirring occasionally, for 10 minutes.
4. Sprinkle the flour into the pan and stir it into the mushrooms with a wooden spoon. Set aside for the moment.
5. Remove the potatoes and onion from the stock mixture with a slotted spoon. Purée them in a blender or food processor or push through a sieve with a wooden spoon.
6. Return the purée to the stock mixture. Add the mushrooms.

7. Bring to the boil, stirring constantly. Stir in the mint.
8. Remove from the heat and stir in the milk.

Brown Lentil Soup G W & Y

Serves 6–8

450 g (1 lb) brown lentils
1 litre (1¼ pints) water
30 ml (2 tablespoons) sunflower oil
1 large onion, peeled and finely chopped
2 garlic cloves, crushed
1.4 litres (2½ pints) vegetable stock
2 sticks celery, trimmed and chopped
1 large carrot, peeled and chopped
1 bay leaf
freshly ground black pepper

1. Place the lentils and water in a pan and bring to the boil. Boil for 2 minutes, then remove from the heat and leave to stand for 2 hours, covered. Drain.
2. Heat the oil in a saucepan and lightly brown the onion. Add the garlic and mix well.
3. Stir in the drained lentils, add the stock and bring to the boil.
4. Add the celery, carrot, bay leaf and pepper.
5. Simmer for 45–60 minutes until the lentils are tender, then remove the bay leaf.
6. Half or all the soup can be puréed in a blender or food processor.

Chilled Tomato Soup G & W

Serves 4

450 g (1 lb) tomatoes, skinned, seeded and chopped
100 g (4 oz) cucumber, peeled and chopped
1 clove garlic, crushed

pinch of cayenne
5 ml (1 teaspoon) Worcestershire sauce
1 medium green pepper, cored, seeded and chopped
150 g (5 oz) natural yogurt
chopped fresh parsley to garnish

1. Place the tomatoes, cucumber, garlic, cayenne, Worcestershire sauce, half the green pepper and half the yogurt in a blender or food processor and liquidize until smooth.
2. Chill well.
3. Stir in the remaining green pepper and yogurt and sprinkle with parsley before serving.

Leek and Potato Soup G W & Y

Serves 4

15 ml (1 tablespoon) sunflower oil
2 carrots, peeled and sliced
2 leeks, trimmed, washed and sliced
1 large potato, peeled and sliced
freshly ground black pepper
450 ml (¾ pint) vegetable stock
150 ml (¼ pint) skimmed milk
4 small sprigs of watercress to garnish

1. Heat the oil in a saucepan. Add the carrots and leeks, cover and sweat over a low heat for 15 minutes.
2. Add the potato slices, pepper to taste and 300 ml (½ pint) of the stock. Bring to the boil and simmer until the potatoes are soft.
3. Liquidize and return to the saucepan, adding the remaining stock and the milk. Adjust the seasoning and serve hot or cold with watercress to garnish.

Bean and Carrot Soup G W & Y

Serves 4

15 ml (1 tablespoon) sunflower oil
450 g (1 lb) carrots, peeled and sliced
1 large potato, diced
1 medium onion, chopped
900 ml (1½ pints) water
15 ml (1 tablespoon) tomato purée
good pinch of ground coriander
freshly ground black pepper
415 g (15 oz) can kidney beans, drained
chopped fresh parsley to garnish

1. Heat the oil in a saucepan, add the vegetables and cook, stirring, for 5 minutes.
2. Add the water, tomato purée, coriander and pepper to taste and bring to the boil. Lower the heat, cover and simmer for 45 minutes.
3. Stir in the kidney beans and reheat gently.
4. Pour into individual soup bowls, garnish with parsley and serve at once.

Chicken and Spinach Soup G W & Y

Serves 4

2 chicken breasts, skinned and each chopped into 8 pieces
600 ml (1 pint) water
10 ml (2 teaspoons) sunflower oil
1 onion, finely chopped
150 g (5 oz) spinach, stalks removed and leaves shredded
freshly ground black pepper
600 ml (1 pint) skimmed milk

1. Place the chicken and water in a saucepan, bring to the boil and simmer for 45 minutes.
2. Heat the oil and gently fry the onion for 2 minutes until translucent.
3. Remove the onion with a slotted spoon and add to the chicken and liquid.
4. Add the spinach, season with black pepper to taste, and cook for a further 5 minutes.
5. Add the milk and heat through before serving.

Fish Soup G & W

Serves 6

1.8 litres (3 pints) fish stock
4 medium onions, peeled and finely chopped
1 medium green pepper, seeded and thinly sliced
1 tablespoon paprika
900 g (2 lb) filleted white fish cut into 5 cm (2 inch) pieces
1 red chilli, chopped finely
75 ml (3 fl oz) sour cream

1. Bring the fish stock to the boil.
2. Reduce the heat and add the onions, pepper and paprika and stir well.
3. Cover the pan and simmer the mixture for 1 hour, or until the onions are soft.
4. Remove the pan from the heat and strain the mixture. Discard any pulp left in the strainer.
5. Add the fish to the strained stock and bring to the boil. Add the chilli, reduce the heat and simmer for 15 to 20 minutes or until the fish flakes easily when tested with a fork.
6. Transfer the soup to a warmed tureen. Stir in the sour cream and serve immediately.

13

FISH

Tuna Jackets W

Serves 4

15 ml (1 tablespoon) sunflower oil
1 red *and* 1 yellow *and* 1 green pepper, cored, seeded and
   diced
60 ml (4 tablespoons) white wine vinegar
30 ml (2 tablespoons) wholegrain mustard
200 g (7 oz) can tuna in oil, drained and flaked
100 g (4 oz) can sweetcorn, drained
4 hot baked potatoes
freshly ground black pepper

1. Heat the oil, add the diced peppers and sauté for 5 minutes. Add the vinegar and mustard and cook for 5 minutes, stirring.
2. Stir in the flaked tuna and sweetcorn.
3. Cut the tops off the potatoes and scoop out the centres. Chop the potato and stir it into half the pepper relish mixture. Season wth black pepper to taste.
4. Spoon the potato mixture back into the potato jackets. Serve the remaining relish separately.

Prawn Provençale G W & Y

Serves 4

50 g (2 oz) margarine
30 ml (2 tablespoons) olive oil
4 shallots, finely chopped
1 garlic clove, crushed (optional)
6 tomatoes, blanched, peeled and chopped
50 g (2 oz) tomato purée
1 teaspoon dried thyme
1 pinch dried basil
freshly ground black pepper to taste
675 g (1½ lb) cooked peeled prawns

1. In a large frying-pan, heat the margarine with the oil. Add the shallots and garlic and fry them for 4 minutes.
2. Add the tomatoes, tomato purée, thyme, basil and pepper to taste. Cover the pan, reduce the heat to low and simmer for 20 minutes. Stir in the prawns and cook uncovered for a further 4 minutes.
3. Remove from the heat and serve at once.

Tuna Surprise G & W

Serves 2–3

15 ml (1 tablespoon) sunflower oil
1 large onion, chopped
1 garlic clove, chopped
½ teaspoon curry powder
225 g (8 oz) can tomatoes
225 g (8 oz) can tuna in oil, drained well
1 teaspoon dried basil
2 tablespoons sultanas *or* seedless raisins
freshly ground black pepper

1. In a medium saucepan, heat the oil, add the onion and garlic and fry for 5 minutes or until the onion is soft and translucent.

2. Stir in the curry powder and add the tomatoes with their juice, tuna, basil, sultanas and pepper to taste.
3. Bring to the boil, reduce the heat to low and simmer gently for 10 minutes.
4. Serve with rice, pasta or potatoes, and vegetables.

Japanese Sardines G & W

Serves 4

100 ml (4 fl oz) soy sauce
50 ml (2 fl oz) vinegar
30 ml (2 tablespoons) lemon juice
25 g (1 oz) fresh root ginger, peeled and chopped
2 garlic cloves, crushed
450 g (1 lb) fresh sardines, washed thoroughly in cold water and dried

1. In a small mixing bowl, combine the soy sauce, vinegar, lemon juice, ginger and garlic.
2. Arrange the sardines in a shallow baking dish and pour the soy sauce mixture over them. Leave in a cool place to marinate for 1½–2 hours.
3. Remove the sardines from the marinade and discard the marinade.
4. Grill for 3–5 minutes or longer, depending on the size, turning once. Serve immediately.

Halibut Fruit G W & Y

Serves 2

grated rind and juice of 2 oranges *and* 1 lemon, *plus* 1 orange, peeled, segmented and skinned, *plus* extra slices for garnish
2 halibut steaks, cut in half

1. Place the grated rind in an ovenproof dish with the juices. Add the fish and baste well. This can be left to marinate for 1–6 hours, turning occasionally.
2. Cover the dish with foil and cook in a pre-heated oven at 180°C (350°F) gas mark 4 for 10 minutes.
3. Add the orange segments and cook for a further 10 minutes.
4. Garnish with a slice of lemon and orange.

Almond Trout G W & Y

Serves 4

4 trout, cleaned, with heads and tails intact
freshly ground black pepper
juice of 1 lemon
25 g (1 oz) margarine
50 g (2 oz) flaked almonds
4 sprigs parsley to garnish

1. Season the fish with pepper and lemon juice.
2. Melt the margarine and lightly brush the fish.
3. Place the fish under a hot grill and cook for 6 minutes each side.
4. Brush one side again lightly with melted margarine and arrange almonds over the fish. Grill again for 1 minute or until the almonds start to brown.
5. Garnish with parsley and serve.

Plaice with Yogurt and Nuts W & Y

Serves 4

675 g (1½ lb) plaice fillets
2 bananas, sliced
75 g (3 oz) unsalted peanuts *plus* 25 g (1 oz) peanuts, crushed, for garnish

Sauce
50 g (2 oz) margarine
50 g (2 oz) plain flour
300 ml (½ pint) milk
3 tablespoons natural yogurt
freshly ground black pepper

1. Place the fish in a greased, shallow ovenproof dish, cover and cook in a pre-heated oven at 180°C (350°F) gas mark 4 for 10 minutes.
2. Remove the fish from the oven and arrange the banana and nuts over the fish.
3. Melt the margarine in a pan and stir in the flour. Cook for 1 minute and gradually add the milk until the sauce thickens. Remove from the heat and add the yogurt.
4. Season the fish with pepper to taste.
5. Pour the sauce over the fish and return to the oven for 15 minutes.
6. Garnish with the finely chopped nuts.

Broccoli and Sweetcorn Stuffed Plaice W & Y

Serves 4

4 plaice fillets
freshly ground black pepper

Stuffing
50 g (2 oz) broccoli tops
50 g (2 oz) cooked brown rice
25 g (1 oz) canned sweetcorn
15 ml (1 tablespoon) lemon juice (fresh)
4 slices lemon to garnish

1. Pre-heat the oven to 180°C (350°F) gas mark 4.
2. Skin the plaice fillets and sprinkle them with black pepper to taste.

3. Cook the broccoli tops, drain well and chop.
4. Place the broccoli, rice and sweetcorn in a bowl and mix well with a little lemon juice.
5. Divide the mixture between the 4 plaice fillets, roll up and secure with a cocktail stick.
6. Place in an ovenproof dish, cover and bake for 25–30 minutes, until the fish is tender.
7. Place on a warm plate, remove the cocktail sticks, and garnish with a slice of lemon to serve.

Mackerel with Lemon Stuffing G W & Y

Serves 4

4 × 175 g (6 oz) mackerel, split and boned
juice of half a lemon
freshly ground black pepper
45 ml (3 tablespoons) water
4 slices lemon to garnish

Stuffing
10 ml (2 teaspoons) sunflower oil
1 small onion, finely chopped
125 g (4 oz) cooked brown rice
finely grated rind *and* juice of a lemon
1 tablespoon freshly chopped parsley
1 small egg (size 4), beaten

1. Pre-heat the oven to 160°C (325°F) gas mark 3.
2. First prepare the stuffing. Heat the oil in a pan, add the onion and cook for 5 minutes or until golden.
3. Transfer to a mixing bowl and combine with the remaining stuffing ingredients.
4. Place the mackerel on a flat surface and sprinkle the flesh with lemon juice and black pepper.
5. Spoon the stuffing into the fish and reshape.

6. Place in an ovenproof dish and add the 3 tablespoons of water.
7. Cover and poach for 15–20 minutes.
8. Garnish with the lemon slices.

Haddock Florentine G W & Y

Serves 2

2 × 150 g (5 oz) haddock portions
225 g (8 oz) fresh or frozen spinach, defrosted and drained
30 ml (2 tablespoons) lemon juice (fresh)
2 slices lemon to garnish

1. Pre-heat the oven to 190°C (375°F) gas mark 5.
2. Place each haddock portion on a piece of aluminium foil.
3. Cover each portion with half the spinach and 1 tablespoon of lemon juice and wrap in the foil.
4. Bake for 20–30 minutes.
5. Remove the foil and serve with a slice of lemon to garnish.

Haddock Kedgeree G W & Y

Serves 2

175 g (6 oz) unsmoked haddock, filleted and skinned
75 g (3 oz) brown rice
1 hard-boiled egg, chopped
½ green pepper, cored, seeded and chopped
2 tablespoons low-fat natural yogurt
1 small onion, finely chopped
1 sprig parsley, chopped
freshly ground black pepper to taste
2 slices lemon to garnish

1. Cover the fish with water in a shallow pan. Heat gently and poach for 8–10 minutes.

2. Remove the fish and flake.

3. Boil the rice in the poaching water left in the pan for about 10 minutes. See cooking instructions on the rice packet. You may need to add extra water.

4. Drain the rice, stir in the fish, egg, green pepper, yogurt, onion and parsley and mix well. Heat gently, stirring all the time.

5. Season with pepper and serve garnished with lemon.

Red Mullet in Tomato Sauce G W & Y

Serves 6

60 ml (4 tablespoons) sunflower oil
1.1 kg (2½ lb) tomatoes, blanched, peeled, seeded and
    coarsely chopped
1 teaspoon dried thyme
1 bay leaf
1 teaspoon freshly ground black pepper
225 g (8 oz) black olives, stoned
2 lemons, cut into 12 slices
6 medium red mullet, cleaned and scaled but with heads and
    tails left on

1. In a large frying pan heat the oil. Add the tomatoes, thyme, bay leaf and pepper. Reduce the heat to low and cook, stirring occasionally, for 15–20 minutes or until the sauce is very thick.

2. Add the olives and lemon slices and stir well. Transfer half the mixture to another frying pan.

3. Place 3 fish in each pan and turn them over in the sauce until they are well coated.

4. Cover the pans and cook, turning the fish occasionally, for 15–20 minutes or until the flesh flakes easily when it is tested with a fork.

5. Discard the bay leaf and serve.

Fish Stew with Peppers G W & Y

Serves 4

30 ml (2 tablespoons) sunflower oil
450 g (1 lb) canned peeled tomatoes
1 red chilli, seeded and finely chopped
2 green peppers, cored, seeded and sliced
2 medium onions, finely chopped
3 garlic cloves, crushed
50 ml (2 fl oz) dry white wine (avoid on a yeast-free diet)
1 teaspoon dried thyme
1 bay leaf
900 g (2 lb) sole fillets, cut into 2.5 cm (1 inch) cubes
450 g (1 lb) small new potatoes, scrubbed, cooked until just
    tender and kept warm

1. In an ovenproof dish heat the oil and add the tomatoes,
   including the juice, and the chilli. Stirring occasionally, cook
   for 15 minutes or until the mixture is thick.
2. Stir in the green peppers, onions, garlic, wine, thyme, bay
   leaf and fish cubes. Cover the dish, reduce the heat to low,
   and cook for 10 minutes, stirring occasionally.
3. Add the potatoes and turn them over in the fish mixture.
   Cover again and cook for a further 5 minutes, until the fish
   flakes easily when tested with a fork.
4. Discard the bay leaf and serve at once.

Fish Pudding W & Y

Serves 4

100 g (4 oz) margarine
25 g (1 oz) fine dry white breadcrumbs
2 tablespoons plain flour
1 teaspoon cornflour
300 ml (½ pint) milk
450 g (1 lb) halibut steaks, poached, skinned, boned and
    flaked

225 g (8 oz) cod fillets, poached, skinned, boned and flaked
1 teaspoon freshly ground black pepper
pinch cayenne
pinch dried dill
finely grated rind of 1 lemon
4 eggs, separated

1. Pre-heat the oven to 180°C (350°F) gas mark 4.
2. Grease a 1.7 litre (3 pint) soufflé or baking dish with some of the margarine. Sprinkle in the breadcrumbs. Press them lightly on the bottom and sides of the dish.
3. In a pan melt half the remaining margarine. Stir in the plain flour and cornflour with a wooden spoon to make a smooth paste. Gradually stir in the milk, avoiding the sauce turning lumpy.
4. Cook the sauce for 2–3 minutes, stirring constantly, until it thickens. Do not allow the sauce to boil.
5. Remove the pan from the heat and set aside. Beat the fish and the remaining margarine in a large mixing bowl until the mixture is well combined. Stir in the sauce. Beat in the black pepper, cayenne, dill, lemon rind and egg yolks.
6. In a separate bowl, beat the egg whites with a rotary whisk until they form stiff peaks. Carefully fold the egg whites into the fish mixture. Spoon the mixture into the prepared dish and place in a roasting tin half filled with hot water.
7. Place the tin in the centre of the oven and bake the pudding for 45–50 minutes or until it is golden brown on top.
8. Remove the tin from the oven and lift out the dish. Serve the pudding immediately.

Salmon Potato Cakes G W & Y

Serves 4

450 g (1 lb) can salmon
200 g (7 oz) potatoes, coarsely grated
1 egg, lightly beaten
3 green shallots, sliced
10 ml (2 teaspoons) vegetable oil

Sauce
5 ml (1 teaspoon) lemon juice (fresh)
13 g (½ oz) sachet vegetable soup mix

1. Drain the salmon and reserve the liquid. Remove bones and skin from salmon.
2. Place the salmon in a bowl and mix in the potatoes, egg and shallots. Divide the mixture into 8 portions and pat into the desired shape.
3. For the sauce, combine the reserved salmon liquid and enough water to measure 100 ml (4 fl oz). Place in a small saucepan with the lemon juice and bring to the boil. Then stir in the soup mix.
4. Heat the oil in a frying pan, add the cakes and fry on each side until golden brown and firm. Serve with the sauce.

Fish Moussaka W & Y

Serves 4

2 large aubergines
175 ml (6 fl oz) vegetable oil
30 ml (2 tablespoons) sunflower oil
2 small onions, finely chopped
225 g (8 oz) cod fillets, cooked, skinned and flaked
450 g (1 lb) halibut steaks, cooked, skinned and flaked
400 g (14 oz) canned tomatoes, chopped
pinch of cayenne
pinch of dried thyme
1 teaspoon dried dill
freshly ground black pepper to taste
1 tablespoon paprika
100 g (4 oz) Cheddar cheese, grated

Sauce
25 g (1 oz) margarine
2 tablespoons plain flour
350 ml (12 fl oz) milk
4 egg yolks
15 ml (1 tablespoon) lemon juice

1. Pre-heat the oven to 190°C (375°F) gas mark 5.
2. Cut the aubergines into slices.
3. In a large frying pan heat 50 ml (2 fl oz) of the vegetable oil, over a moderate heat. Add about one third of the aubergine slices and fry for 3–4 minutes on each side or until they are golden brown.
4. Remove with a spatula and allow to drain on kitchen paper. Fry the remaining slices in the same way, adding more oil as necessary. Set aside.
5. Heat the sunflower oil over a moderate heat. Add the onions and cook, stirring occasionally, for 5–7 minutes.
6. Stir in the fish, tomatoes and their juice, cayenne, thyme, dill, pepper and paprika. Cook, stirring frequently, for 3 minutes. Remove the pan from the heat and set aside.

7. Arrange one third of the aubergine on the bottom of an ovenproof dish. Spoon over them half the fish and tomato mixture. Sprinkle half the cheese over the top.

8. Cover with another third of the aubergine slices and cover that with the remaining fish and tomato mixture. Sprinkle remaining cheese over the top.

9. Cover with the remaining aubergine slices. Set aside.

10. To make the sauce, melt the margarine in a medium saucepan over a moderate heat.

11. Remove the pan from the heat and, with a wooden spoon, stir in the flour to make a smooth paste.

12. Gradually stir in the milk, being careful to avoid lumps.

13. Return the pan to the heat and cook, stirring constantly, for 2–3 minutes until it is very thick and smooth.

14. Cool the sauce. When cooled, beat in the egg yolks. Stir in the lemon juice.

15. Pour the sauce over the aubergine slices to cover them completely.

16. Place the dish in the centre of the oven and bake for 35–40 minutes or until the top is golden brown. Serve immediately.

Fisherman's Pie W

Serves 4

450 g (1 lb) potatoes
350 g (12 oz) haddock *or* cod fillet
100 g (4 oz) mushrooms
225 g (8 oz) can tinned tomatoes
freshly ground black pepper
10 ml (2 teaspoons) oil
1 medium onion, chopped
50 g (2 oz) margarine
50 g (2 oz) plain flour
200 ml (⅓ pint) skimmed milk
100 g (4 oz) peeled prawns (optional)
1 medium tomato, thinly sliced

1. Pre-heat the oven to 180°C (350°F) gas mark 4.
2. Boil and mash the potatoes.
3. Cut the fish into large pieces and place them in a casserole dish. Cover with the mushrooms, tomatoes and a little of the tomato juice from the can, and season with pepper to taste.
4. Heat the oil and gently fry the onion.
5. Melt the margarine in a saucepan, add the flour and stir for 1 minute. Gradually add the milk and stir until the sauce thickens. Stir in the cooked onion.
6. Add the prawns to the saucepan and pour the sauce over the fish.
7. Cover with the mashed potato and arrange the sliced tomato over the top.
8. Cook for 30 minutes until golden.

14

MEAT

Steaks with Mixed Herbs G & W

Serves 4

4 rump steaks about 2 cm (¾ inch) thick
freshly ground black pepper to taste
50 g (2 oz) margarine
2 tablespoons freshly chopped parsley
1 tablespoon freshly chopped tarragon
1 tablespoon freshly chopped chives
50 g (2 oz) finely chopped mushrooms
50 ml (2 fl oz) milk

1. Place the steaks on a board and sprinkle with pepper. Set aside.
2. Melt the margarine in a large frying pan over a moderate heat. Add the steaks, parsley, tarragon, chives and mushrooms and fry for 2 minutes on each side, stirring constantly.
3. Reduce the heat and cook for a further 2 minutes on each side. Double the time for well-done steaks.
4. Remove the steaks from the pan and transfer to a warmed serving dish. Keep them hot while you make the sauce.
5. Pour the milk into the pan and cook for 2 minutes, stirring constantly until the mixture is hot but not boiling.
6. Remove the pan from the heat, pour the sauce over the steaks and serve immediately.

Steak and Bananas W & Y

Serves 6

1 egg, well beaten
75 g (3 oz) fresh white breadcrumbs
6 firm bananas, peeled and cut into 1.5 cm (½ inch) slices
50 g (2 oz) margarine
6 fillet steaks
15 ml (1 tablespoon) vegetable oil
freshly ground black pepper to taste
225 ml (8 fl oz) horseradish sauce (if not on low-yeast diet)

1. Pre-heat the grill on high.
2. Pour the egg into a shallow dish and place the breadcrumbs on a plate.
3. Dip the banana slices in the egg and then coat them with the breadcrumbs. Set aside.
4. In a large frying pan melt the margarine over a moderate heat and fry the banana slices for 3 minutes, turning once.
5. Remove from the pan with a slotted spoon and drain excess fat on kitchen paper. Keep the bananas hot while you cook the steaks.
6. Brush the steaks with the oil and sprinkle with pepper. Place the steaks on a rack under the grill and grill for 2 minutes each side. Reduce the heat and cook for a further 2 minutes each side. Double the cooking time for well-done steaks.
7. Transfer the steaks to a warmed serving dish, arrange the bananas around them and serve immediately with the horseradish sauce.

Sussex Casserole W & Y

Serves 4–5

900 g (2 lb) potatoes, peeled and thickly sliced
900 g (2 lb) lean braising steak, cut into 2.5 cm (1 inch)
  cubes
2 medium onions, peeled and finely chopped
6 sticks celery, trimmed and chopped
450 g (1 lb) pickling onions
8 green olives, stoned
freshly ground black pepper to taste
1 teaspoon grated nutmeg
4 whole cloves (optional)
15 ml (1 tablespoon) apple juice
450 ml (1 pint) vegetable stock
1 tablespoon cornflour dissolved in water

1. Pre-heat the oven to 180°C (350°F) gas mark 4.
2. Cover the bottom of an ovenproof casserole with half of the potato slices.
3. Arrange half the steak cubes on top and cover with the onions, celery, pickling onions and olives. Sprinkle with black pepper and nutmeg.
4. Add the cloves (optional).
5. Cover with the remaining steak and potatoes.
6. Mix the apple juice, stock and cornflour mixture.
7. Pour over the meat, vegetables and potato. Cover and cook for 2½ hours. Remove the lid and increase the heat to 200°C (400°F) gas mark 6 for a further 30 minutes, or until the potatoes are tender and golden brown. Remove from the oven and serve at once. Remove cloves (if used).

Beef and Bean Casserole G W & Y

Serves 4

450 g (1 lb) black-eyed beans, soaked for 12 hours
1.4 litres (2½ pints) cold water
15 ml (1 tablespoon) sunflower oil
2 large onions, finely chopped
2 garlic cloves, crushed
900 g (2 lb) stewing beef, cut into 2.5 cm (1 inch) cubes
1 bay leaf
½ teaspoon dried marjoram
4 large tomatoes, blanched, peeled and sliced
175 ml (6 fl oz) vegetable stock
freshly ground black pepper
1 green pepper, cored, seeded and chopped

1. Pre-heat the oven to 180°C (350°F) gas mark 4.
2. Drain the beans, add fresh water and bring to the boil. Reduce the heat and simmer for 1½ hours, or until the beans are tender.
3. Drain the beans, reserving all the liquid.
4. Heat the oil and gently fry the onions and garlic for 5 minutes, stirring occasionally. Remove from the pan with a slotted spoon and place to one side.
5. Raise the heat, add the cubes of beef and cook until browned all over. Remove from the pan and place in an ovenproof dish.
6. Add to the beef the onions, garlic, bay leaf, marjoram, tomatoes and beef stock, and season with fresh black pepper to taste.
7. Cover and cook for 2 minutes.
8. Remove the casserole from the oven and add the beans, chopped pepper and reserved liquid.
9. Return to the oven and cook for a further hour, stirring occasionally.

Pork Chops with Tomatoes and Mushrooms G & W

Serves 4

4 boned loin pork chops
30 ml (2 tablespoons) vegetable oil
1 teaspoon dried thyme
1 tablespoon margarine
100 g (4 oz) mushrooms, sliced
400 g (14 oz) canned tomatoes, chopped
1 teaspoon dried sage
1 tablespoon chopped fresh parsley
freshly ground black pepper to taste

1. Pre-heat the grill on a high heat.
2. Brush the chops with the oil. Sprinkle the thyme and pepper over them. Lay the chops on the rack in the grill pan.
3. Grill the chops for 5 minutes each side. Reduce the heat and cook for 15–20 minutes on each side, depending on the thickness of the chops, or until they are thoroughly cooked.
4. Meanwhile make the sauce. In a large frying pan, melt the margarine over a moderate heat. Add the mushrooms and fry for 3 minutes, stirring occasionally.
5. Add the tomatoes with their juices, the sage, parsley and pepper to taste.
6. Cover the pan and cook on a low heat for 15 minutes.
7. Remove the chops from the grill and arrange in a warmed serving dish. Spoon the sauce over the meat and serve immediately.

Pork with Cranberry Sauce W

Serves 4

4 large boned pork chops, trimmed of excess fat
25 g (1 oz) seasoned flour made with 25 g (1 oz) white
   flour, pinch of cayenne and ½ teaspoon dried rosemary
1 tablespoon margarine
15 ml (1 tablespoon) vegetable oil
60 ml (4 tablespoons) canned cranberries
150 ml (5 fl oz) dry white wine
freshly ground black pepper to taste
30 ml (2 tablespoons) milk

1. Dip the chops in the seasoned flour and coat thoroughly on all sides. Shake off any excess flour.
2. Melt the margarine with the oil in a large frying pan. Add the pork chops and fry for 5 minutes each side, or until they are well browned.
3. Reduce the heat and continue cooking the chops for 20–30 minutes or until they are thoroughly cooked and tender.
4. Transfer the chops to a warmed serving dish and keep the chops hot whilst you make the sauce.
5. Remove the frying pan from the heat and pour off all the fat except 1 tablespoon.
6. Return the pan to the heat and stir in the cranberries, wine and pepper. Bring to the boil. Cook the sauce for 5 minutes, stirring occasionally.
7. Stir in the milk and pour the sauce over the chops. Serve immediately.

Dutch Pork W

Serves 6–8

450 g (1 lb) loin pork, boned and trimmed of excess fat
1 teaspoon black pepper
½ teaspoon mustard
2 teaspoons dried sage
2 tablespoons raisins
1 large cooking apple, peeled, cored and thinly sliced
15 ml (1 tablespoon) apple juice
50 g (2 oz) margarine
700 g (25 oz) canned apricots in fruit juice, drained and
    juice reserved
1½ teaspoons cornflour, dissolved in water

1. Pre-heat the oven to 180°C (350°F) gas mark 4.
2. Place the loin of pork on a work surface and rub with the
    pepper, mustard and sage.
3. Lay the meat fat side down and sprinkle with half the
    raisins. Cover the raisins with apple slices and sprinkle
    with the remaining raisins.
4. Roll the meat and tie with string at 2.5 cm (1 inch)
    intervals.
5. In a large roasting tin, melt the margarine over a
    moderate heat. Place the pork in the tin and fry, turning
    the meat from time to time for 8 minutes or until it is
    browned all over.
6. Remove the roasting tin from the heat and place in the
    centre of the oven. Roast the meat, basting occasionally,
    for 2½ hours or until it is tender and the juices run clear
    when the meat is pierced with a sharp knife.
7. Fifteen minutes before the meat is cooked, pre-heat the
    grill on a high heat. Arrange the apricots in a heatproof
    dish, sprinkle with the apple juice and place under the
    grill for 5–6 minutes until the tops of the apricots are
    pale brown. Remove the dish and keep warm.
8. Remove the roasting tin from the oven and transfer the

pork to a carving dish. Remove the string from the meat and arrange the apricots around the pork. Keep warm while you prepare the sauce.

9. Pour off most of the pork fat from the tin, leaving about 3 tablespoons. Place the tin over a moderate heat and pour in the reserved apricot juice. Stir in the cornflour mixture and bring the sauce to the boil, stirring constantly.

10. Remove the sauce from the heat and strain the sauce into a warmed sauce boat. Serve immediately with the meat.

Piquant Pork Chops W

Serves 4

4 pork chops, trimmed of excess fat
2 garlic cloves, crushed
½ teaspoon dried basil
50 ml (2 fl oz) sunflower oil
100 ml (4 fl oz) dry cider
30 ml (2 tablespoons) wine vinegar
15 ml (1 tablespoon) apple juice
½ teaspoon freshly ground black pepper
½ teaspoon cayenne
3 large carrots, peeled and sliced on the diagonal
½ cucumber, sliced on the diagonal
1 green pepper, cored, seeded and cut into strips
1 tablespoon cornflour, dissolved in 4 tablespoons water

1. Rub the pork chops all over with the garlic and basil. Set aside.
2. In a large frying pan heat the oil and fry the chops for 5 minutes on each side. Cover the pan, reduce the heat to low and cook the chops for 30 minutes.
3. Transfer the chops to a plate and set aside. Pour off all but 2 tablespoons of the juice and return to a moderate heat.

4. Stir in the cider, vinegar, apple juice, pepper and cayenne and bring the sauce to the boil, stirring constantly.
5. Mix in the vegetables, cover the pan and cook for 2 minutes.
6. Remove the pan from the heat and stir in the cornflour mixture. Return to the heat and, stirring constantly, cook for 1 minute until the sauce is thick and translucent.
7. Return the chops to the pan and baste well with the sauce. Cover the pan and simmer for 5 minutes.
8. Transfer the chops to a warm serving dish and pour the sauce and vegetables over them.

Herb-Baked Gammon W & Y

Serves 4

1.4 kg (3 lb) middle leg of gammon, washed, soaked in
   cold water overnight and drained
2 tablespoons chopped fresh parsley
1 teaspoon dried basil
1 tablespoon chopped mint
1 teaspoon dried thyme
1 tablespoon chopped fresh chives
1 tablespoon grated lemon rind
1 teaspoon grated orange rind
freshly ground black pepper to taste
50 g (2 oz) fresh white breadcrumbs
1 egg, lightly beaten

1. Pre-heat the oven to 170°C (325°F) gas mark 3.
2. Cover the gammon in foil, twisting the edges, and place on a rack in a roasting tin half filled with water.
3. Bake for 2½ hours, turning the gammon over halfway through.
4. Remove the gammon and allow to rest in foil for 30 minutes. (Keep the oven on.)
5. In a bowl, mix together the remaining ingredients and put to one side.

6. Using a sharp knife, remove most of the rind and fat from the gammon joints.

7. Press the herb mixture firmly into the joint with your fingertips.

8. Bake for a further 10–15 minutes. Serve either immediately, or cold with salad.

Lamb and Parsley Stew W & Y

Serves 4

30 ml (2 tablespoons) vegetable oil
1 garlic clove, crushed (optional)
1 large onion, sliced
450 g (1 lb) boned shoulder of lamb, trimmed of excess fat and cubed
600 ml (1 pint) vegetable stock
4 tablespoons finely chopped fresh parsley
1 bay leaf
6 large tomatoes, blanched, peeled and chopped
4 tablespoons tomato purée
2 carrots, scraped and sliced
225 g (8 oz) can red kidney beans, drained
1 tablespoon cornflour, dissolved in 2 tablespoons water

1. Heat the oil in a medium-sized flameproof casserole and then add the garlic, onion and lamb cubes. Fry for 7 to 8 minutes, stirring constantly until the meat is brown on all sides.

2. Stir in the stock, parsley, bay leaf, tomatoes, tomato purée and carrots and bring to the boil. Cover and simmer for 1 hour.

3. Add the kidney beans and cornflour mixture to the stew and stir well. Simmer for 15 minutes, or until the lamb is tender and the sauce is thick. Remove the bay leaf and serve immediately.

Lamb and Apricot Pilaff G & W

Serves 4

30 ml (2 tablespoons) sunflower oil
1 medium onion, thinly sliced
700 g (1½ lb) boned leg of lamb, cut into 2.5 cm (1 inch) cubes
75 g (3 oz) dried apricots, soaked overnight, drained and halved
3 tablespoons raisins
½ teaspoon ground cinnamon
freshly ground black pepper
900 ml (1½ pints) water
225 g (8 oz) long-grain rice, washed, soaked in cold water for 30 minutes and drained

1. Heat the oil in a frying pan, add the onion and cook for about 5 minutes, until translucent but not brown.
2. Add the lamb and cook, stirring and turning occasionally, for 5–8 minutes, or until it is lightly browned all over. Stir in the apricots, raisins, cinnamon and pepper.
3. Pour in half of the water and bring to the boil, stirring occasionally. Reduce the heat to low, cover the pan and simmer the meat for 1–1¼ hours, or until the meat is tender when pierced with the point of a sharp knife.
4. Cook the rice in the usual way, using the remaining water.
5. Pre-heat the oven to 180°C (350°F) gas mark 4.
6. Place one third of the meat in a medium ovenproof casserole. Cover with a layer of one third of the rice mixture, then top with another one third of the meat. Continue to make the layers in this manner until all the ingredients have been used up, finishing with a layer of rice. Cover the casserole and bake for 50 minutes. Serve immediately.

Lamb in a Spicy Yogurt Sauce G W & Y

Serves 4

225 ml (8 fl oz) water
15 ml (1 tablespoon) olive oil
3 onions, sliced
900 g (2 lb) leg of lamb, boned and cut into 2 cm
   (¾ inch) cubes
freshly ground black pepper
2 garlic cloves, crushed
1 teaspoon chopped fresh parsley
600 ml (1 pint) yogurt
1 tablespoon cornflour mixed to a paste with 10 ml
   (2 teaspoons) water
1 teaspoon grated lemon rind
1 tablespoon chopped fresh coriander leaves (dried can
   be used)

1. In a large saucepan, bring the water and oil to the boil over moderate heat.
2. Add the onions, lamb, pepper, garlic and parsley. Cover the pan tightly, reduce the heat to low and simmer for 1¼ hours or until the lamb is very tender and the liquid has reduced by about two thirds of its original quantity.
3. In a medium saucepan, heat the yogurt and cornflour mixture over a moderate heat, stirring constantly. Reduce the heat to very low and cook for 8 minutes or until it has reduced by half its original quantity.
4. Add the yogurt mixture and the lemon rind to the lamb mixture, stir well and simmer, uncovered, for 15 minutes.
5. Add the coriander and serve with a crisp salad and boiled rice.

Lamb Chops with Rosemary G W & Y

Serves 4

45 ml (3 tablespoons) olive oil
30 ml (2 tablespoons) lemon juice (fresh)
freshly ground black pepper
2 teaspoons dried rosemary
1 garlic clove, crushed
4 thick lamb chops

1. In a medium-sized shallow mixing bowl combine the oil, lemon juice, pepper to taste, rosemary and garlic.
2. Place the lamb chops in the marinade and baste them well. Set aside in a cool place and marinate for 1–2 hours, basting frequently.
3. Pre-heat the grill to high. Place the lamb chops on the grill rack. Reserve the marinade. Grill the chops for 2 minutes on each side, basting them frequently with the marinade, or until they are tender when pierced with the point of a sharp knife.
4. Remove the chops from the grill and place them on a warmed serving plate. Spoon the warmed marinade over the chops and serve immediately.

Spiced Liver G W & Y

Serves 4

700 g (1½ lb) lamb's liver, thinly sliced
5 cm (2 inch) piece of fresh ginger, peeled and finely grated
4 garlic cloves, crushed
1 teaspoon hot chilli powder
freshly ground black pepper
juice of 1 lemon
15 ml (1 tablespoon) sunflower oil

1. Cut each liver slice in half lengthways. Set aside.
2. Combine the ginger, garlic, chilli powder, pepper and lemon juice in a mixing bowl. Add the liver slices and turn and toss them in the mixture until they are all well coated. Cover the bowl and set aside to marinate for 1 hour.
3. In a large frying pan, heat the oil over a moderate heat. When the oil is very hot add the liver slices, a few at a time, and fry, turning them frequently, for 4–6 minutes or until they are crisp and tender. Using a slotted spoon, remove the liver from the pan and set it aside on a warmed serving dish. Keep hot while you fry the remaining slices in the same way.

Liver and Sweetcorn W & Y

Serves 2

15 ml (1 tablespoon) sunflower oil
50 g (2 oz) chopped onions
1 small garlic clove, chopped
300 g (10 oz) liver
100 g (4 oz) can sweetcorn, drained
60 ml (4 tablespoons) vegetable stock
pinch of thyme
freshly ground black pepper to taste

1. Heat the oil in a frying pan and add the onions and garlic. Sauté for a couple of minutes until the onions are soft.
2. Add the liver and cook, turning occasionally, until browned.
3. Add the sweetcorn and cook for 1 minute longer.
4. Stir in the remaining ingredients and bring to the boil.
5. Reduce the heat, cover and simmer for 2 minutes.

Liver Kebabs G W & Y

Serves 4

700 g (1½ lb) lamb's liver, thickly sliced
15 ml (1 tablespoon) lemon juice (fresh)
freshly ground black pepper to taste
75 ml (3 fl oz) olive oil
4 tablespoons cumin seeds
3 medium onions, thinly sliced

1. Pre-heat the grill on a moderate heat.
2. Sprinkle the liver with lemon juice and set aside for 10 minutes. Pat dry with kitchen paper and rub the liver with black pepper. Brush the liver with 30 ml (2 tablespoons) of the oil.
3. Place the meat on foil and grill for 2 minutes each side. Transfer to a chopping board.
4. With a sharp knife cut the liver into 5 cm (2 inch) cubes.
5. Roll the cubes in the cumin seeds. Thread the cubes of liver on to skewers and roll them again in the cumin seeds. Set aside and keep warm.
6. Heat the remaining olive oil in a frying pan. Add the onions and cook stirring occasionally, for 5–7 minutes until they are soft.
7. Place the skewers under the grill and grill the kebabs for 4–6 minutes, turning occasionally, until the liver is tender and cooked through. Serve on a plate and cover with the onions.

Kidneys in Sesame Sauce G & W

Serves 2 as a main course, 4 as a starter

4 pig's kidneys, cleaned and prepared
300 ml (½ pint) water
4 tablespoons peanut butter
45 ml (3 tablespoons) vegetable oil
15 ml (1 tablespoon) sesame oil
30 ml (2 tablespoons) soy sauce
45 ml (3 tablespoons) sherry (optional)
2 teaspoons sugar
1 pinch cayenne
2 leeks, white part only, finely chopped

1. Cut each kidney into 6 slices lengthways.
2. In a small saucepan bring the water to the boil and drop the kidney slices in. When they change colour remove the pan from the heat and drain the kidneys. Set aside.
3. In a small bowl mix together the peanut butter, 1 tablespoon of the vegetable oil, the sesame oil, soy sauce, sherry (if using), sugar and cayenne. Set the sauce aside.
4. In a large frying-pan, heat the remaining vegetable oil over moderate heat. Add the kidneys and leeks and cook them for 4 minutes, stirring constantly.
5. Using a slotted spoon, remove the kidneys and leeks from the pan. Drain them on kitchen paper and place them on a heated serving dish. Pour the sauce over the kidneys and leeks. Serve immediately.

POULTRY

Chicken and Spinach Stir-fry G & W

Serves 2

45 ml (3 tablespoons) vegetable oil
225 g (8 oz) chicken, cut into strips
30 ml (2 tablespoons) soy sauce
15 ml (1 tablespoon) apple juice
freshly ground black pepper to taste
40 g (1½ oz) margarine
450 g (1 lb) spinach, washed, trimmed and chopped

1. Heat the oil and add the chicken strips. Stir-fry for 2 minutes.
2. Add the soy sauce, apple juice and pepper and stir-fry for a further 2 minutes. With a slotted spoon transfer the chicken to a plate.
3. Add 25 g (1 oz) of the margarine to the pan and melt over a moderate heat. Add the spinach and stir-fry for 3 minutes. Add the remaining margarine and fry for a further 30 seconds.
4. Transfer the spinach with a slotted spoon to a warmed serving dish.
5. Increase the heat and return the chicken to pan. Stir-fry for 30 seconds to reheat thoroughly.
6. Pour the chicken and the pan juices over the spinach and serve immediately.

Chicken with Peach Sauce G W & Y

Serves 4

freshly ground black pepper
1.6 kg (3½ lb) fresh chicken, skinned and cut into
   6 serving pieces
60 ml (2 tablespoons) vegetable oil
1 small onion, finely chopped
1 garlic clove, crushed
¼ teaspoon red pepper flakes
½ teaspoon ground ginger
225 ml (8 fl oz) vegetable stock
50 ml (2 fl oz) lime juice
50 ml (2 fl oz) lemon juice
15 ml (1 tablespoon) sunflower oil
4 fresh peaches, washed, dried, halved, stoned and sliced

1. Pre-heat the oven to 190°C (375°F) gas mark 5.
2. Sprinkle the black pepper over the chicken pieces and set them aside.
3. In a large frying pan heat the oil and add the chicken pieces a few at a time. Fry, turning occasionally, for 8–10 minutes. With a slotted spoon, remove the chicken from the pan and transfer to a medium ovenproof casserole.
4. Add the onion and garlic to the pan and fry them, stirring occasionally, for 5–7 minutes or until the onion is soft and translucent but not brown. Stir in the pepper flakes, ginger and stock and bring the mixture to the boil, stirring constantly.
5. Remove the pan from the heat and stir in the lime and lemon juice. Pour the mixture over the chicken pieces in the casserole. Set aside.
6. Melt the oil in a clean frying pan and gently fry the peaches for 6 minutes, or until they begin to pulp. Transfer from the pan to the casserole.

7. Cover the casserole and bake in pre-heated oven for 1 hour or until the chicken pieces are tender. Serve with rice.

Grilled Chicken with Herbs G W & Y

Serves 4

2 × 900 g (2 lb) chickens, cut in half lengthways
1 large garlic clove, halved
½ teaspoon freshly ground black pepper
100 g (4 oz) sunflower margarine
30 ml (2 tablespoons) olive oil
juice of ½ lemon
1 tablespoon chopped fresh parsley
1½ teaspoons dried basil

1. Pre-heat the grill to moderate. Rub the chicken halves all over with the garlic clove and then with the pepper, and set aside.
2. In a small saucepan heat the margarine and oil. Remove from the heat and stir in the lemon juice, parsley and basil.
3. Brush the chicken with the oil and herb mixture, place the chicken halves skin side down on the grill and grill for 7–10 minutes on each side, basting frequently with the oil and herb mixture.
4. After 15 minutes, test the chicken halves by inserting a skewer into one of the thighs. If the juices run clear, they are cooked.
5. Remove the chicken halves from the grill, transfer to a warmed serving dish and spoon any remaining oil and herb mixture over them.

Sweet and Sour Chicken G

Serves 4

350 g (12 oz) chicken breast
pinch of Chinese five spice powder
2 tablespoons flaked almonds
350 g (12 oz) fresh pineapple without skin *or* canned in
    natural juice
50 ml (2 fl oz) wine vinegar
15 ml (1 tablespoon) shoyu soy sauce
1 tablespoon arrowroot
45 ml (3 tablespoons) sunflower oil
4 spring onions, chopped
1 garlic clove, thinly sliced
1 dessertspoon thinly sliced ginger root
1 green pepper, cored, seeded, and cut into long strips

1. Slice the chicken into small, thin slices and sprinkle them
    with five spice powder.
2. Toast the almonds under the grill until they are lightly
    browned.
3. Blend 100 g (4 oz) of the pineapple with the wine vinegar,
    soy sauce and arrowroot. Cut the remaining pineapple
    into 2.5 cm (1 inch) chunks and reserve.
4. Heat 1 tablespoon of the oil in a wok or frying pan and stir
    in the onions, garlic and ginger. Fry for 1 minute and
    remove to a plate.
5. Heat the rest of the oil in the pan and toss the chicken
    slices in it until just browned, 3–5 minutes.
6. Add the pepper and stir for about 1 minute. Add the
    cooked onion, garlic and ginger, pineapple chunks and
    toasted almond flakes.
7. Pour the pineapple and vinegar liquid over the top and
    stir for a few minutes. Serve immediately.

Hot Fruity Chicken G

Serves 2

15 ml (1 tablespoon) concentrated apple juice
1 garlic clove, chopped
2 teaspoons peeled, grated ginger
10 ml (2 teaspoons) chilli sauce
300 g (10 oz) chicken breast, skinned and boned, and
    cut into thin strips
10 ml (2 teaspoons) sunflower oil
150 g (5 oz) sliced onions
1 medium green pepper, cored, seeded and chopped
1 teaspoon cornflour
freshly ground black pepper
2 large oranges, peeled, segmented and pith removed

1. Mix together the apple juice, half the garlic, the ginger
    and the chilli sauce. Add the chicken and coat
    thoroughly.
2. Cover and refrigerate for at least 1 hour to marinate. It
    can be left overnight.
3. Remove the chicken and reserve the marinade.
4. Heat the oil and sauté the onions and remaining garlic
    until the onions are translucent.
5. Add the chicken and chopped pepper and cook until the
    chicken is lightly browned on both sides.
6. Strain the reserved marinade and mix it with the
    cornflour.
7. Add the cornflour mixture and black pepper to taste to
    the pan. Bring to the boil, stirring constantly. Reduce the
    heat to a simmer.
8. Add the orange segments and heat through thoroughly,
    stirring occasionally. Serve immediately.

Chicken with Almonds G & W

Serves 4–6

30 ml (2 tablespoons) vegetable oil
1 × 2.2 kg (5 lb) chicken, cut into 8 serving pieces
1 large onion, finely chopped
2 garlic cloves, crushed (optional)
1 large green pepper, seeded and chopped
1 large red pepper, seeded and chopped
425 ml (15 fl oz) chicken stock
1 pinch of cayenne pepper
bouquet garni, consisting of 4 parsley sprigs, 1 thyme spray
    and 1 bay leaf tied together
2 hard-boiled egg yolks
50 g (2 oz) ground almonds

1. Heat the oil in a large flameproof casserole over a moderate heat. Add the chicken and brown gently on both sides.
2. Remove the chicken and set aside.
3. Add the onion, garlic and green pepper. Stir occasionally for 5–7 minutes or until the onion is soft but not brown.
4. Add the chicken to the casserole with the stock, cayenne and bouquet garni. Bring the liquid to the boil, reduce heat and simmer for 40 minutes or until the chicken pieces are tender.
5. In a small bowl mash the egg yolks and 3 tablespoons of the cooking liquid together with a fork until the mixture forms a smooth paste. Add the ground almonds and combine the mixture thoroughly.
6. Stir the paste into the casserole a little at a time, simmer for a further 10 minutes.
7. Remove the chicken pieces from the casserole and transfer to a warmed serving dish. Discard the bouquet garni, and continue to boil the sauce stirring occasionally

for 3–5 minutes until it has thickened slightly.

8. Remove the casserole from the heat and pour the sauce over the chicken. Serve immediately.

Chicken with Grapes and Peanuts G & W

Serves 6–8

30 ml (2 tablespoons) groundnut oil
900 g (2 lb) chicken breasts, cut into 2.5 cm (1 inch) cubes
freshly ground black pepper to taste
65 g (2½ oz) unsalted peanuts, ground
30 ml (2 tablespoons) soy sauce
good pinch of mild chilli powder
450 g (1 lb) seedless white grapes, halved
75 g (3 oz) unsalted peanuts, finely chopped and toasted

1. Heat the oil over a moderate heat. Add the chicken and cook for 5 minutes, or until the cubes are browned.
2. Add the pepper, ground peanuts, soy sauce and chilli powder and mix well.
3. Reduce the heat and add the grapes. Simmer for 15–20 minutes, until the chicken is tender.
4. Remove from the heat and transfer to a warmed serving dish. Sprinkle with the chopped peanuts and serve.

Turkey Breast with Mushroom Sauce W

Serves 4

30 ml (2 tablespoons) vegetable oil
1 medium onion, finely chopped
1 garlic clove, crushed (optional)
4 turkey breasts
25 g (1 oz) margarine
400 g (14 oz) mushrooms, wiped clean and sliced
450 ml (16 fl oz) chicken stock
1 teaspoon chopped fresh thyme *or* ½ teaspoon dried thyme
freshly ground black pepper to taste
1 bay leaf
2 tablespoons cornflour, dissolved in 90 ml
     (6 tablespoons) water

1. Heat the oil in a frying pan and add the onion, garlic and turkey breasts. Cook, turning frequently, for 8–10 minutes until evenly brown.
2. Remove the onion, garlic and turkey and set aside. Drain off the oil and add the margarine to the pan with the mushrooms. Stir constantly for 3 minutes. Remove from the pan and set aside.
3. In a large flameproof casserole, heat the stock, thyme, pepper and bay leaf. Stir in the cornflour mixture. Stir constantly until the mixture begins to thicken.
4. Add the turkey, onion, garlic and mushrooms to the casserole, stir well.
5. Reduce heat to low, cover and simmer for 20–25 minutes or until the turkey is tender. Remove bay leaf and serve.

Turkey and Chickpeas with Rice G W & Y

Serves 4

50 g (2 oz) margarine
12 pickling onions
900 g (2 lb) turkey breast, cut into 2.5 cm (1 inch) cubes
100 g (4 oz) chickpeas, soaked overnight and drained
225 ml (8 fl oz) vegetable stock
freshly ground black pepper
1 teaspoon ground cumin seeds
pinch of turmeric
450 g (1 lb) long-grain rice, washed, soaked in cold water
    for 30 minutes and drained

1. Melt the margarine in a large pan over a moderate heat. Add the onions and turkey cubes and cook, stirring and turning, for 5–8 minutes, until the onions are golden.
2. Add the chickpeas, stock and enough water to cover the mixture completely.
3. Add the pepper to taste, cumin and turmeric to the pan and stir well to blend. Cover the pan and cook for 1¼ hours or until the turkey and chickpeas are tender.
4. Raise the heat and bring the liquid to the boil. Stir in the rice. Cover the pan, reduce the heat and simmer for 15–20 minutes or until the rice is tender and the liquid absorbed.
5. Remove the pan from the heat, spoon the mixture into a warmed serving dish and serve immediately.

Parsley and Lemon Stuffing G W & Y

Enough to stuff a 4–4.5 kg (9–10 lb) chicken or turkey

300 g (10 oz) cooked brown rice
grated rind *and* juice of 2 lemons
4 tablespoons chopped fresh parsley
1 teaspoon grated orange rind
¼ teaspoon dried thyme
¼ teaspoon dried marjoram
50 g (2 oz) margarine
75 ml (3 fl oz) orange juice
1 egg (size 3), beaten

1. In a medium mixing bowl combine the rice, lemon rind, parsley, orange rind, thyme, marjoram and margarine.
2. Stir in the orange juice, lemon juice and egg and blend well.
3. Stuff the chicken or turkey in the usual way.

16

EGG AND VEGETARIAN DISHES AND SAVOURY SAUCES

Spanish Rice G & W

Serves 3–4

45 ml (3 tablespoons) olive oil
2 onions, thinly sliced
2 garlic cloves, crushed
1 green pepper, cored, seeded and thinly sliced
2 red peppers, cored, seeded and thinly sliced
350 g (12 oz) mushrooms, thinly sliced
400 g (14 oz) canned, chopped tomatoes
40 g (1½ oz) stoned green olives (optional)
1 teaspoon dried oregano
½ teaspoon basil
freshly ground black pepper to taste
150 g (5 oz) cooked rice

1. Heat the oil in a large frying pan. Add the onions and garlic and cook for 5–7 minutes, stirring occasionally.
2. Add the green and red peppers and cook for 4 minutes, stirring frequently. Add the mushrooms, tomatoes with their juice, olives, oregano, basil and pepper to the pan and cook, stirring occasionally, for 3 minutes.
3. Add the rice to the pan and cook for 3–4 minutes, stirring constantly until the rice is heated through.
4. Serve immediately, if serving hot.

Nut Croquettes W & Y

Serves 4

25 g (1 oz) sunflower margarine
1 small onion, finely chopped
25 g (1 oz) plain flour *plus* 2 tablespoons
150 ml (5 fl oz) milk
100 g (4 oz) unsalted peanuts, finely chopped
1 small carrot, peeled and finely grated
¼ teaspoon dried thyme
¼ teaspoon freshly ground black pepper
60 ml (4 tablespoons) sunflower oil

1. Melt the margarine in a saucepan, add the onion and cook until soft.
2. Stir in 25 g (1 oz) of the flour to make a smooth paste.
3. Remove the pan from the heat and, stirring constantly, gradually add the milk. Return to the heat and, stirring constantly, bring to the boil. Boil for 1 minute until very thick.
4. Remove the pan from the heat and add the peanuts, carrot, thyme and pepper and mix thoroughly.
5. Spoon into a medium dish and set aside to cool.
6. Cut the mixture into 5 × 2.5 cm (2 × 1 inch) pieces and roll them in the remaining flour.
7. In a large frying pan heat the oil. When hot, add half the croquettes and fry for 4 minutes until golden brown. Remove from the frying pan with a slotted spoon on to kitchen paper. Keep them warm while you cook the remaining croquettes.

Spiced Lentil Cakes W & Y

Serves 5

225 g (8 oz) green lentils
vegetable oil for frying
1 garlic clove, crushed
2 carrots, peeled and chopped
1 small onion, chopped
2 teaspoons ground coriander
2 teaspoons ground cumin seeds
finely grated rind *and* juice of ½ orange
3 tablespoons fresh chopped parsley
50 g (2 oz) fresh, white breadcrumbs
freshly ground black pepper
2 eggs (size 3), beaten
50 g (2 oz) dry white breadcrumbs, sieved
parsley
wedges of lemon

1. Cook the lentils in boiling water for 30–35 minutes. Drain and refresh under cold water. Drain thoroughly again.
2. Meanwhile, heat 30 ml (2 tablespoons) vegetable oil in a pan. Add the garlic, carrots and onion. Cover and cook gently, shaking the pan occasionally, for 15 minutes. Cool.
3. Place the lentils and vegetables in a blender or food processor with the coriander, cumin, orange rind and juice and blend until smooth. Transfer to a bowl, stir in the parsley and fresh breadcrumbs, and season with black pepper.
4. Divide the mixture into 10 portions and form into flat cakes, pressing firmly to remove any cracks. Dip the cakes into the beaten egg and then in the dry breadcrumbs. Chill for 30 minutes.
5. Heat 6 mm (¼ inch) vegetable oil in a frying pan and fry the lentil cakes for 3–4 minutes on each side until golden brown. Garnish with parsley and lemon wedges.

Vegetable and Dal Jackets W

Serves 4

30 ml (2 tablespoons) vegetable oil
1 small onion, chopped
1 tablespoon mild curry powder
75 g (3 oz) red lentils
75 g (3 oz) French beans, trimmed and cut into 2.5 cm
    (1 inch) lengths
50 g (2 oz) raisins
25 g (1 oz) desiccated coconut
200 ml (7 fl oz) vegetable stock
400 g (14 oz) canned, chopped tomatoes
4 hot baked potatoes
freshly ground black pepper
toasted, flaked coconut to garnish

1. Heat the oil and sauté the onion for 3 minutes, until soft.
2. Add the curry powder and lentils and cook for 5 minutes, stirring occasionally.
3. Add the beans, raisins, coconut, stock and tomatoes, cover and simmer for 20 minutes, stirring frequently.
4. Cut the tops off the potatoes and scoop out the centres. Cut the potato into chunks, add to the vegetable dal and season with black pepper.
5. Spoon a little of the vegetable mixture into the potato skins and serve the remainder separately.
6. Garnish with a little toasted coconut.

Chickpea Dips W & Y

Serves 8

2 × 350 g (15 oz) cans chickpeas, drained and rinsed
1 garlic clove, crushed
15 ml (1 tablespoon) lemon juice (fresh)
25 ml (1 fl oz) olive oil
175 ml (6 fl oz) Greek plain yogurt
freshly ground black pepper
4 teaspoons freshly chopped parsley
10 ml (2 teaspoons) tomato purée
sprigs of parsley *and* strips of red pepper *and* pieces of
   sliced lemon to garnish
selection of raw vegetables – peppers, radishes, carrots,
   celery, cucumber – to serve

1. Place the chickpeas in a blender or food processor and blend until smooth.
2. Add the garlic, lemon juice, olive oil and yogurt and mix well. Add black pepper to taste.
3. Transfer one third of the mixture to a small serving bowl. Divide the rest between 2 small mixing bowls.
4. Add the chopped parsley to one, stir well and transfer to a small serving bowl.
5. Add the tomato purée to the other, stir well and transfer to a small serving bowl. Adjust seasoning if necessary.
6. Garnish the herb dip with sprigs of parsley, the tomato dip with red pepper and the plain dip with pieces of lemon.
7. Chop the vegetables into sticks. Arrange on a serving dish around the dips.

Egg and Vegetable Bake G W & Y

Serves 6

15 ml (1 tablespoon) olive oil
2 medium onions, finely chopped
2 garlic cloves, crushed
6 large tomatoes, peeled and finely chopped
1 green chilli, seeded and finely chopped
5 ml (1 teaspoon) apple juice
freshly ground black pepper
½ teaspoon ground coriander
12 eggs
175 g (6 oz) Cheddar cheese, grated
1 tablespoon margarine
pinch of chilli powder

1. Pre-heat the oven to 230°C (450°F) gas mark 8.
2. Heat the oil in a large frying pan. Add the onions and garlic and fry for 5–7 minutes, stirring occasionally.
3. Add the tomatoes, chilli, apple juice, pepper and coriander to the pan. Reduce the heat and simmer the mixture, stirring frequently, for 15–20 minutes or until it is soft and pulpy.
4. Transfer the mixture to a large ovenproof dish.
5. With the back of a spoon, make 12 hollows in the mixture. Break one egg into each hollow.
6. Sprinkle the cheese over the eggs. Dot the margarine over the cheese and sprinkle the chilli powder over the top.
7. Bake in the centre of the oven for 6–8 minutes or until the cheese is golden brown and the eggs have set.
8. Serve immediately.

Courgette and Tomato Quiche W & Y

Serves 4–6

225 g (8 oz) shortcrust pastry
50 g (2 oz) margarine
2 garlic clove, crushed
4 courgettes, trimmed and sliced
freshly ground black pepper to taste
½ teaspoon oregano
100 ml (4 fl oz) milk
3 eggs
50 g (2 oz) Cheddar cheese, grated
5 small tomatoes, peeled and thinly sliced

1. Line a flan dish with the pastry and set aside.
2. Pre-heat the oven to 200°C (400°F) gas mark 6.
3. Melt the margarine in a large frying pan.
4. Add the garlic and fry, stirring frequently, for 1 minute.
5. Add the courgettes and pepper. Fry for 8–10 minutes or until lightly browned.
6. Remove the pan from the heat and add the oregano, mixing well to blend.
7. In a mixing bowl combine the milk, eggs and cheese. Beat well to blend.
8. Arrange the courgettes and tomatoes in circles in the pastry flan case.
9. Pour the egg, milk and cheese mixture over the courgettes and tomatoes.
10. Place in the centre of the oven and bake for 35–45 minutes or until the filling is set and golden brown.

Potato and Cheese Bake W & Y

Serves 4

700 g (1½ lb) potatoes, peeled
50 g (2 oz) margarine
2 medium onions, finely chopped
25 g (1 oz) plain flour
freshly ground black pepper to taste
½ teaspoon dried mixed herbs
350 ml (12 fl oz) milk
225 g (8 oz) Cheddar cheese, finely grated

1. Pre-heat the oven to 180°C (350°F) gas mark 4.
2. Boil and mash the potatoes. Place them in a medium mixing bowl and set aside.
3. With a teaspoon of the margarine, grease a medium ovenproof dish.
4. Melt the remaining margarine in a saucepan over a moderate heat. Add the onions and fry until softened and golden.
5. Remove the pan from the heat and with a wooden spoon stir in the flour, black pepper and herbs to make a smooth paste.
6. Gradually add the milk, stirring constantly and being careful to avoid lumps.
7. Return the pan to a low heat, stirring constantly, for 4–5 minutes or until the sauce is smooth and thick.
8. Add 175 g (6 oz) of the cheese and cook until it has melted, stirring all the time.
9. Gradually pour the cheese sauce over the potatoes, beating constantly with a wooden spoon until the mixture is smooth.
10. Turn the mixture into the prepared dish and smooth the mixture down with the back of a spoon. Sprinkle with the remaining cheese.
11. Place the dish in the centre of the oven and bake for

20–25 minutes or until the top is golden brown. Serve immediately.

Mexican Stuffed Eggs G & W

Serves 6

6 hard-boiled eggs
1 medium avocado, peeled, stoned and chopped
1 small onion, finely minced
1 small green pepper, cored, seeded and finely minced
100 g (4 oz) prawns *or* shrimps, shelled, deveined and
    finely chopped, *or* almond halves, finely chopped
5 ml (1 teaspoon) lemon juice
5 ml (1 teaspoon) wine vinegar
freshly ground black pepper to taste
1 pinch of cayenne pepper
1 tablespoon chopped parsley

1. Slice the eggs in half lengthways and scoop out the yolks. Set the whites aside. Using the back of a wooden spoon rub the yolks and the avocado flesh through a fine nylon strainer into a medium-sized mixing bowl. Stir in the onion, green pepper and chopped nuts or prawns.
2. Add the lemon juice, vinegar, pepper and cayenne, mixing well to blend.
3. With a teaspoon, generously stuff the egg white halves with the mixture. Arrange on a serving dish, sprinkle with parsley and chill before serving.

Nut and Vegetable Loaf G W & Y

Serves 4–6

10 ml (2 teaspoons) sunflower oil
1 small onion, chopped
1 small carrot, chopped
1 stick celery, chopped
15 ml (1 tablespoon) tomato purée
225 g (8 oz) tomatoes, skinned and chopped
2 eggs
1 tablespoon chopped parsley
freshly ground black pepper
225 g (8 oz) nuts, finely chopped or minced
onion rings
parsley sprigs

1. Pre-heat the oven to 220°C (425°F) gas mark 7.
2. Melt the oil in a pan, add the onion, carrot and celery and cook until softened. Add the tomato purée and tomatoes and cook for 5 minutes.
3. Put the eggs, parsley and pepper to taste in a bowl and beat well. Stir in the nuts and vegetables.
4. Transfer to a greased 900 ml (1½ pint) ovenproof dish and bake for 30–35 minutes.
5. Turn out and decorate with onion rings and parsley. Serve hot with vegetables and sauce, or cold with salad.

Peanut Savoury Pie G & W

Serves 4

30 ml (2 tablespoons) groundnut oil
1 large onion, sliced
225 g (8 oz) roasted peanuts, chopped
225 g (8 oz) can tomatoes
5 ml (1 teaspoon) Worcestershire sauce
1 teaspoon chopped mixed herbs
freshly ground black pepper
225 g (8 oz) shortcrust pastry
1 egg, beaten

1. Pre-heat the oven to 200°C (400°F) gas mark 6.
2. Heat the oil in a frying pan, add the onion and fry for about 10 minutes until softened. Stir in the nuts, tomatoes with their juice, Worcestershire sauce, herbs and pepper to taste. Bring to the boil and simmer for 2–3 minutes. Remove from the heat and leave to cool.
3. Divide the prepared pastry in half. Roll out one piece on a floured surface and use to line a 20 cm (8 inch) pie plate. Spoon in the filling. Roll out the remaining pastry and cover the pie. Glaze with beaten egg. Knock up the edges, seal well and flute.
4. Bake for 35–40 minutes, until golden. Serve hot or cold, with vegetables of your choice or salad.

Bean and Tomato Hot-Pot G & W

Serves 4

30 ml (2 tablespoons) sunflower oil
2 onions, sliced
3 carrots, sliced
2 sticks celery, sliced
1 large leek, sliced
2 garlic cloves, crushed
415 g (15 oz) can red kidney beans, drained
400 g (14 oz) can tomatoes
300 ml (½ pint) stock
1 tablespoon yeast extract
freshly ground black pepper
750 g (1½ lb) potatoes, thinly sliced
15 g (½ oz) margarine

1. Pre-heat the oven to 180°C (350°F) gas mark 4.
2. Heat the oil in a flameproof casserole, add the onions and fry for 5 minutes. Add the carrots, celery, leek and garlic and fry for a further 5 minutes.
3. Add the kidney beans, tomatoes with their juice, stock, yeast extract, and pepper to taste. Mix well.
4. Arrange the potatoes neatly on top, sprinkling pepper between each layer. Dot with the margarine, cover and cook in the oven for 2 hours.
5. Remove the lid 30 minutes before the end of cooking to allow the potatoes to brown.

Bean and Egg au Gratin Y

Serves 4

450 g (1 lb) shelled broad beans
3 hard-boiled eggs, sliced
50 g (2 oz) margarine
40 g (1½ oz) wholewheat flour
450 ml (¾ pint) milk
freshly ground black pepper
2 tablespoons fresh brown breadcrumbs
50 g (2 oz) Cheddar cheese, grated

1. Pre-heat the oven to 220°C (425°F) gas mark 7.
2. Cook the beans in boiling water until just tender, and drain. Put half the beans in a greased ovenproof dish, place the eggs on top and cover with the remaining beans.
3. Melt 40 g (1½ oz) of the margarine in a pan, stir in the flour and cook gently, stirring. Remove from the heat and gradually add the milk, stirring continuously. Return to the heat and bring to the boil. Cook, stirring, until thickened. Season to taste with pepper.
4. Pour the sauce over the beans and sprinkle the breadcrumbs and cheese over the top. Dot with the remaining margarine and bake for 15 minutes, until golden brown. Serve immediately.

Oaty Cheese Quiche W

Serves 4–6

Pastry
75 g (3 oz) self-raising flour
150 g (5 oz) fine oatmeal
freshly ground black pepper
100 g (4 oz) vegetable margarine
dried beans for baking 'blind'

Filling
350 g (12 oz) cottage cheese, sieved
2 tablespoons natural yogurt
6 sticks celery, chopped
75 g (3 oz) hazelnuts, chopped
pinch of curry powder

Garnish
pinch of paprika
tomato slices
parsley sprigs

1. Pre-heat the oven to 200°C (400°F) gas mark 6.
2. Mix the flour and oatmeal together, with freshly ground pepper to taste. Cut in the margarine and rub in until the mixture resembles breadcrumbs. Stir in enough water to make a fairly stiff pastry and knead together lightly.
3. Turn on to a floured surface, roll out and use to line a 23 cm (9 inch) flan ring. Cover the base with greaseproof paper and fill with dried beans. Bake 'blind' for 20 minutes. Remove the paper and beans and return the flan to the oven for 5 minutes. Allow to cool.
4. Mix the cheese, yogurt, celery, nuts and curry powder together and pile into the flan case. Sprinkle with paprika and garnish with tomato and parsley.

Corn and Asparagus Flan Y

Serves 4–6

225 g (8 oz) wholewheat pastry
dried beans for baking 'blind'
198 g (7 oz) can sweetcorn, drained
141 g (5 oz) can asparagus tips, drained
1 small onion, chopped
75 g (3 oz) Cheddar cheese, grated
2 large eggs, beaten
300 ml (½ pint) milk
freshly ground black pepper

1. Pre-heat the oven to 200°C (400°F) gas mark 6.
2. Roll out the prepared pastry and line a 20 cm (8 inch) flan tin. Cover the base with greaseproof paper and fill with dried beans. Bake 'blind' for 10 minutes. Remove the paper and beans and bake for a further 15 minutes.
3. Mix the sweetcorn, asparagus, onion, cheese, eggs and milk together. Add pepper to taste and pour into the prepared flan case.
4. Lower the oven temperature to 190°C (375°F) gas mark 5 and return the flan to the oven for 30 minutes until set. Serve hot or cold.

Potato and Herb
Omelette W & Y

Serves 4

450 g (1 lb) potatoes, cooked and mashed
3 eggs, separated
30 ml (2 tablespoons) milk
1 tablespoon mixed herbs
freshly ground black pepper
10 ml (2 teaspoons) sunflower oil
cucumber and tomato slices

1. Beat the potato with the egg yolks, milk, mixed herbs and pepper to taste.
2. Whisk the egg whites until stiff and fold them into the potato mixture.
3. Heat the oil in an omelette pan, add the mixture and cook for 2 minutes on each side.
4. Slide on to a serving plate and cut into quarters. Garnish each portion with cucumber and tomato. Serve with green salad or vegetables.

Spinach and Tomato Omelette G W & Y

Serves 1

2 eggs (size 3)
freshly ground black pepper
1 teaspoon sunflower oil
50 g (2 oz) fresh spinach, cooked in a little boiling water
    for 3–4 minutes, and drained
2 medium tomatoes, sliced

1. Beat the eggs and mix with pepper to taste.
2. Heat the oil in a frying pan, pour in the egg mixture and
    leave to set for ½ minute.
3. Add the spinach and tomato and leave for about a minute
    until heated through.
4. Fold in half and serve.

Baked Nutty Onions G W & Y

Serves 4

300 g (10 oz) sliced onions
1 bay leaf
300 ml (½ pint) skimmed milk
25 g (1 oz) sunflower margarine
25 g (1 oz) rice or potato flour
freshly ground black pepper
1 teaspoon ground nutmeg
150 g (5 oz) unsalted peanuts, finely chopped
2 tomatoes, halved and grilled

1. Pre-heat the oven to 190°C (375°F) gas mark 5.
2. Place the onion, bay leaf and milk in a saucepan and bring
    to the boil. Cover, and simmer for 10 minutes.
3. Strain the milk into a jug, discard the bay leaf and place
    the onion in a greased ovenproof dish.

4. Melt the margarine in a small pan. When foaming, stir in the flour and cook for 1 minute. Gradually add the milk, stirring continuously. Cook until thick and smooth. Add pepper and nutmeg to taste.

5. Pour the sauce over the onions and sprinkle evenly with nuts. Bake for 20–30 minutes. Reduce the heat if the nuts are browning too quickly. Garnish with the tomatoes.

Nutty Sprout Stir-fry G & W

Serves 2–4

75 g (3 oz) unsalted peanuts
1 medium orange, peeled and cut into segments
10 ml (2 teaspoons) oil
1 pinch of cayenne
½ teaspoon ground cumin seeds
2 thick spring onions, trimmed and sliced
1 garlic clove, thinly sliced
175 g (6 oz) Brussels sprouts, trimmed and thinly sliced
1 red pepper, cored, seeded and thinly sliced
30 ml (2 tablespoons) soy sauce (avoid for low-yeast diet)

1. Place the peanuts on a baking dish in a pre-heated oven (190°C/375°F, gas mark 5) until they are lightly roasted.

2. Slice the orange segments crossways into triangles.

3. Heat the oil in a wok or heavy frying pan. Add the cayenne, cumin, spring onions, garlic and sprouts and toss in the oil for 1 minute.

4. Add the roasted peanuts and red pepper, mix and fry again for 1 minute.

5. Lastly add the orange triangles and soy sauce and stir-fry until all the vegetables are coated and the oranges are heated through. Serve immediately.

Spinach Gratin W & Y

Serves 4

2 slices dry wholewheat bread (or white if on a
    wholewheat-restricted diet)
50 g (2 oz) Gruyère cheese
450 g (1 lb) fresh *or* frozen spinach, cooked and drained well
½ teaspoon grated nutmeg
freshly ground black pepper

1. Pre-heat the oven to 230°C (450°F) gas mark 8.
2. Break up the bread into rough breadcrumbs.
3. Grate the cheese.
4. Mix the spinach with the nutmeg, pepper to taste and half
   the grated cheese, and place in an ovenproof dish.
5. Mix the remaining cheese with the breadcrumbs and
   sprinkle them over the top.
6. Bake for about 15 minutes until golden brown.

Vegetable Curry G & W

Serves 2

10 ml (2 teaspoons) vegetable oil
1 garlic clove, crushed
¼ teaspoon turmeric
¼ teaspoon coriander
¼ teaspoon cumin seeds
1 teaspoon finely chopped ginger
½ small chilli, seeded and finely chopped
30 ml (2 tablespoons) tomato purée
900 ml (1½ pints) vegetable stock
175 g (6 oz) boiled butter beans
75 g (3 oz) cauliflower, broken into florets
75 g (3 oz) turnip, cut into 2.5 cm (1 inch) cubes
75 g (3 oz) parsnip, cut into 2.5 cm (1 inch) cubes
75 g (3 oz) courgettes, thickly sliced
1 small onion, chopped

1. Heat the oil in a saucepan. Add the garlic, spices and chilli, and stir over a moderate heat for 1 minute.
2. Add the all the remaining ingredients, mix well and bring to the boil.
3. Cover and simmer for 15 minutes, then for a further 10 minutes without a lid.
4. Serve with brown rice and salad.

Mustard Sauce G & W

Makes about 300 ml (½ pint)

1 tablespoon margarine
1 garlic clove, crushed
1½ tablespoons rice or potato flour
freshly ground black pepper to taste
300 ml (½ pint) milk
1 tablespoon prepared French *or* German mustard
5 ml (1 teaspoon) lemon juice

1. Melt the margarine in a saucepan over a moderate heat. Add the garlic and cook for 4 minutes.
2. Remove the pan from the heat and stir in the flour with a wooden spoon. Add the pepper and make into a smooth paste. Gradually stir in the milk, avoiding the sauce turning lumpy.
3. Stir in the mustard thoroughly.
4. Cook the sauce over a low heat for 3–4 minutes until it has thickened. Do not let the sauce boil.
5. Remove the pan from the heat and stir in the lemon juice. Pour into a sauce boat and serve immediately.

Orange and Herb Sauce W & Y

Serves 4

10 ml (2 teaspoons) sunflower oil
1 small onion, finely chopped
175 ml (6 fl oz) fresh orange juice
2 teaspoons chopped tarragon
2 teaspoons chopped parsley
freshly ground black pepper
2 teaspoons cornflour
1 orange, peeled, segmented, pith removed and chopped

1. Heat the oil and gently fry the onion. Add the orange juice, herbs and black pepper to taste.
2. Bring to the boil and simmer for 2–3 minutes.
3. Mix the cornflour with 1 tablespoon cold water and stir into the sauce, bringing slowly to the boil and stirring constantly.
4. Add the chopped orange segments, heat for 1–2 minutes and serve.

This sauce can be used to complement meat and fish dishes as well as vegetarian ones, and can be made in larger quantities in advance and frozen.

17

SWEETS, BREADS, PASTRY AND CAKES

Dried Fruit Compote G & W

Serves 2

100 g (4 oz) mixture of dried fruits, e.g. peaches, prunes, apples, apricots and pears
75 ml (5 level tablespoons) orange juice
2 whole cloves
2 × 2.5 cm (1 inch) sticks cinnamon
juice *and* zest of ½ lemon

1. Wash the fruit and place it in a bowl with the orange juice, spices, lemon juice and zest.
2. Leave to soak overnight.
3. Next day, if the juice has been absorbed add 2 tablespoons water. Then place the mixture in a saucepan, bring to the boil, cover and simmer on a very low heat for 10–15 minutes.
4. Transfer to a serving bowl, removing the cinnamon and cloves. Leave to cool or serve warm.

Rhubarb and Ginger Mousse G & W

Serves 4

450 g (1 lb) rhubarb
3 tablespoons clear honey
juice *and* grated rind of ½ orange
¼ teaspoon ground ginger
2 teaspoons powdered gelatine
30 ml (2 tablespoons) water
2 egg whites

1. Trim the rhubarb and chop into 2.5 cm (1 inch) pieces.
2. Put the rhubarb into a pan with the honey, orange juice, rind and the ginger, and simmer gently until the fruit is soft.
3. Dissolve the gelatine in 2 tablespoons of water, placing the bowl in hot water. Stir until the gelatine is dissolved.
4. Add the gelatine mixture to the fruit and beat until smooth.
5. Cool the rhubarb mixture until it is half set.
6. Whisk the egg whites until soft and fold them lightly into the half-set rhubarb mixture.
7. Spoon into decorative glasses and chill until set.

Baked Apple G W & Y

Serves 1

1 cooking apple
1 dessertspoon concentrated apple juice
1 pinch of cinnamon
1 cup water

1. Pre-heat the oven to 180°C (350°F) gas mark 4.

2. Wash and core the apple, and score around the centre in a circle, just breaking the skin.
3. Place the apple in an ovenproof dish.
4. Mix the apple juice with the cinnamon.
5. Pour the water into the dish, and pour the apple juice over the apple.
6. Bake for approximately 50–60 minutes.

Melon Ice Cream G W & Y

Serves 4

1 medium melon (ogen or similar if you can get it)
300 ml (½ pint) plain yogurt
concentrated apple juice to sweeten, if necessary
melon balls to decorate

1. Halve the melon, scoop out the seeds, then scoop out the melon flesh and place it in the blender or food processor.
2. Liquidize the melon flesh and mix with the yogurt and concentrated apple juice as needed.
3. Place the melon and yogurt mixture in a shallow dish and freeze until firm.
4. Scoop the melon ice cream into dessert glasses and decorate with melon balls.

Orange Jelly G W & Y

Serves 8

4 large oranges
2 teaspoons agar powder
100 ml (4 oz) apple juice

1. Cut the oranges in half and scoop out the flesh.
2. Put the empty orange halves to one side.
3. Remove the pith and pips from the orange segments and blend the flesh in a blender or food processor.
4. Mix the agar powder with a little of the apple juice. Pour this into a saucepan with the rest of the apple juice and a little of the blended orange.
5. Bring to the boil and cook gently for 1½ minutes.
6. Take the pan off the heat and add the mixture to the rest of the blended oranges. Mix well.
7. Leave the mixture to cool slightly, then pour it into the 8 orange halves.

Apple Custard G W & Y

Serves 4

450 g (1 lb) eating apples, sliced
150 ml (5 fl oz) water
½ teaspoon ground cinnamon
2 eggs

1. Pre-heat the oven to 180°C (350°F) gas mark 4.
2. Place the apples, water and cinnamon in a saucepan and cook gently until the apple softens and most of the water is absorbed.
3. Blend in a blender or food processor and allow to cool for 5–10 minutes.
4. Whisk the eggs and add a little at a time to the apple juice.
5. Pour the custard into a 20 cm (8 inch) baking dish and bake for 25–30 minutes until browned on top and firm. Serve immediately.

Apple and Passion Fruit Delight G W & Y

Serves 4

4 large eating apples (about 800 g/1¼ lb), chopped
¼ cup water
3 medium passion fruits
1 tablespoon concentrated apple juice
1 teaspoon grated orange rind
3 egg whites

1. Place the apples and water in a saucepan and bring to the boil. Cover, reduce the heat and simmer for 5 minutes or until the apples are tender.
2. Add the passion fruits, apple juice and orange rind and stir well, then leave to cool.
3. Beat the egg whites in a bowl until soft peaks form. Fold this into the apple mixture, and refrigerate for 1 hour before serving.

Fruit Mousse G W & Y

Serves 4

100 ml (4 fl oz) apricot nectar
100 ml (4 fl oz) pear juice
2 teaspoons gelatine
30 ml (2 tablespoons) water
2 teaspoons sugar
1 egg, separated
1 medium fresh peach

1. Mix the two juices and pour into a bowl.
2. Sprinkle the gelatine over the water, dissolve over hot water and allow to cool to room temperature.
3. Mix the sugar, egg yolk and gelatine mixture in a bowl, then add to the bowl containing the fruit juice, and refrigerate until slightly thick.
4. Beat the egg white in a small bowl until soft peaks form. Add to the fruit mixture and fold in lightly.
5. Refrigerate until set and decorate with fresh fruit.

Fresh Fruit Salad G W & Y

Serves 4

1 dessert apple, peeled and sliced
1 banana, peeled and sliced
60 ml (4 tablespoons) lemon juice
1 orange, peeled and segmented
1 grapefruit, peeled and segmented
100 g (4 oz) seedless grapes
2 kiwi fruit, peeled and sliced
30 ml (2 tablespoons) orange juice
4 sprigs mint

1. Toss the apple and banana in the lemon juice. This will prevent discoloration.
2. Combine all the fruits in a serving bowl. Serve chilled and decorate with a sprig of mint.

Baked Bananas G W & Y

Serves 6

6 large bananas unpeeled
15 ml (1 tablespoon) vegetable oil

1. Pre-heat the oven to 170°C (325°F) gas mark 3.
2. Rub the banana skins with the vegetable oil. Brush an oven-proof dish with the remaining oil.
3. Lay the bananas in the dish and place in the centre of the oven.
4. Bake for 30–40 minutes or until they are soft and the skins have turned black.
5. Serve hot with one strip of the skin peeled back.

Banana and Tofu Cream G & W

Serves 4

200 g (7 oz) firm tofu
200 g (7 oz) bananas, skinned
75 g (3 oz) ground almonds
1 pinch of cinnamon
2 teaspoons almond flakes

1. Blend or process the tofu and banana together. To obtain a creamy texture, the mixture may need to be put through a sieve or food mill.
2. Add the ground almonds and mix well.
3. Spoon into 4 bowls or glasses and sprinkle lightly with the cinnamon and a few almond flakes.

Nutty Carob Slice G & W

Makes 8 slices

50 g (2 oz) raisins, chopped and soaked in 25 ml
    (1½ tablespoons) water for 20 minutes
100 g (4 oz) smooth peanut butter (sugar- and salt-free)
25 g (1 oz) carob powder
50 g (2 oz) sesame seeds
25 g (1 oz) sugar-free apricot jam

1. Boil the raisins in the water until the water is absorbed.
2. Mix the peanut butter, carob powder, sesame seeds, jam and raisins together.
3. Press into an 18 cm (7 inch) diameter round tin and chill for 2 hours.
4. Cut into slices and serve.

Apple and Tofu Cheesecake G & W

Makes 12 slices

1 quantity of seed pastry (see page 195)
dried beans for baking 'blind'

Filling
450 g (1 lb) eating apples, chopped
100 ml (4 fl oz) water
200 g (7 oz) firm tofu
1 egg, whisked
30 ml (2 tablespoons) freshly squeezed lemon juice
5 ml (1 teaspoon) vanilla essence
1 teaspoon cinnamon
25 g (1 oz) ground almonds
25 g (1 oz) brown rice flakes

1. Bake the pastry blind in a 23 cm (9 inch) baking tin for 10 minutes in an oven preheated to 180°C (350°F) gas mark 4.
2. Combine the apple with the water and purée in a blender or food processor. Add the tofu and continue to blend until a thick paste is formed.
3. Fold in the whisked egg, lemon juice, vanilla essence, cinnamon and ground almonds.
4. Pour the mixture into the part-baked pastry case and sprinkle with brown rice flakes.
5. Return to the oven at the same temperature for 30 minutes.
6. Serve chilled.

Banana Cake W

Make 16 slices

75 g (3 oz) dried dates
100 ml (4 fl oz) water
225 g (8 oz) banana, finely mashed
1 egg (size 3), whisked
75 g (3 oz) wholewheat flour (white if on a wholewheat-free diet)
25 g (1 oz) soya flour
50 g (2 oz) ground almonds
1 teaspoon bicarbonate of soda
2.5 ml (½ teaspoon) vanilla essence
150 ml (5 fl oz) low-fat natural yogurt

1. Pre-heat the oven to 180°C (350°F) gas mark 4.
2. Cook the dates in the water over a low heat until all the water has been absorbed. Blend in a food processor to a smooth paste.
3. Mix the cooled paste with the banana and egg, then fold in the flours, ground almonds and bicarbonate of soda. Stir in the vanilla essence and yogurt.
4. Lightly grease and flour a 20 cm (8 inch) diameter baking tin and pour in the mixture.
5. Bake for 35–40 minutes until the cake is brown on top and comes away from the tin.

Pineapple Cake G & W

Makes 12 slices

50 g (2 oz) prunes, stoned and finely chopped
25 g (1 oz) dried figs
150 ml (5 fl oz) water
300 g (10 oz) fresh pineapple *or* tinned pineapple in fruit
    juice, drained
25 g (1 oz) raisins
40 g (1½ oz) pumpkin seeds
2 eggs, whisked well
40 g (1½ oz) ground almonds
75 g (3 oz) brown rice flour

1. Pre-heat the oven to 180°C (350°F) gas mark 4.
2. Place the prunes, figs and water in a saucepan and simmer until the water has been absorbed and the fruit is soft. Mash with a fork and leave to cool.
3. Chop the pineapple into 1 cm (½ inch) squares, combine with the raisins and add the dried fruit paste.
4. Grind the pumpkin seeds.
5. Add the egg to the fruit mixture.
6. Fold in the ground almonds, pumpkin seeds and flour.
7. Pour the mixture into a greased and floured 20 cm (8 inch) baking tin.
8. Bake for 40 minutes.

Pancakes G W & Y

Serves 4

50 g (2 oz) rice flour
50 g (2 oz) cornflour
1 small egg
300 ml (½ pint) skimmed milk

1. Make a thin batter with the flour, egg and skimmed milk.

2. Use kitchen paper to wipe a small non-stick frying pan with a little oil and heat oil until it is smoking.
3. Pour a generous 30 ml (2 tablespoons) of batter into the pan and swirl it around to cover base. Cook for 60 seconds.
4. Flip it over and cook for a further few seconds.

Oatcakes W & Y

Makes 12 square oatcakes

50 g (2 oz) oatmeal
50 g (2 oz) oatgerm and bran
15 ml (1 tablespoon) vegetable oil
30 ml (2 tablespoons) concentrated apple juice
20 ml (2 dessertspoons) boiling water

1. Pre-heat the oven to 170°C (325°F) gas mark 3.
2. Combine the oatmeal, oatgerm, bran and oil in a bowl.
3. Add the apple juice and hot water to make a soft doughy mixture.
4. Roll out on a work top lightly dusted with oatmeal.
5. Cut into squares and place on an ungreased baking sheet.
6. Bake for 20–25 minutes.

Rice Noodle Pudding G W & Y

Serves 8–10

375 g (13 oz) broad rice noodles
75 g (3 oz) margarine
3 medium eggs
1 rounded dessertspoon ground cinnamon
1 flat teaspoon ground mixed spice
½ flat teaspoon ground ginger
rind *and* juice of 1 lemon
175 g (6 oz) raisins
50 g (2 oz) sultanas
75 g (3 oz) caster sugar

1. Pre-heat the oven to 180°C (350°F) gas mark 4.
2. Pour boiling water over the noodles and leave covered to stand for 3–4 minutes.
3. Melt the margarine in the oven.
4. Beat the eggs and add in all the dry ingredients, lemon juice and the dried fruit.
5. Pour the mixture over the drained noodles in a large bowl and mix thoroughly, together with the melted margarine.
6. Pour the noodle mixture into a dish and place in the centre of the oven for 40–50 minutes. When ready, it should look golden brown and crispy on the outside but still be soft on the inside.

When cooked it can be served hot as a pudding or may be eaten cold.

Christmas Pudding G W & Y

Makes 1 large pudding or 2 small puddings

2 eggs (size 1)
100 g (4 oz) Flora cooking margarine
100 g (4 oz) alternative breadcrumbs (wheat-, oats- rye *or* barley-free)
50 g (2 oz) brown rice flour
50 g (2 oz) cornflour
100 g (4 oz) molasses
1 large cooking apple, chopped
1 teaspoon cinnamon
1 teaspoon ginger
1 teaspoon mixed spice
225 g (8 oz) raisins
100 g (4 oz) sultanas
100 g (4 oz) currants
50 g (2 oz) mixed candied peel
1 grated carrot
50 g (2 oz) flaked almonds
zest of 1 large orange *and* 1 lemon
45 ml (3 tablespoons) rum
45 ml (3 tablespoons) brandy
45 ml (3 tablespoons) port
1 teaspoon Rite Diet Wheat free baking powder *or* 1 teaspoon cream of tartar
½ teaspoon bicarbonate of soda

1. Lightly grease a 1.2 litre (2 pint) pudding basin or two 600 ml (1 pint) basins.
2. Whisk the eggs and melt the margarine until soft.
3. Blend all the ingredients together and place in the pudding basin(s).
4. Cover with greaseproof paper and a layer of muslin or cotton. Tie with string and bring the sides of the muslin or cotton up and knot to make a handle. This will make it easier to lift out of the pressure cooker when cooked.

5.   Pressure cook the 600 ml (1 pint) basins for 1½ hours each
     and the 1.2 litre (2 pint) basin for 2 hours. Serve with
     brandy butter.

Seed Pastry G & W

15 ml (1 tablespoon) boiling water
50 g (2 oz) dried figs, chopped
25 g (1 oz) sunflower seeds
25 g (1 oz) pumpkin seeds
25 g (1 oz) sesame seeds, toasted
25 g (1 oz) ground hazelnuts
½ teaspoon mixed spice

1.   Leave the figs to stand in the boiling water for 10 minutes.
2.   Purée the figs in a blender or food processor.
3.   Grind all the seeds to powder and combine in a mixing
     bowl with the ground hazelnuts and mixed spice.
4.   Bind the seed mixture with the figs to make a dough. Add
     a little chilled water to bind if necessary.
5.   Roll out and prepare as ordinary pastry. This is an
     excellent sweet, grain-free pastry.

Wheat-free Pastry G W & Y

50 g (2 oz) rice flour
50 g (2 oz) cornflour
1 egg
50 g (2 oz) Cooking Flora

1. Combine all the ingredients and form a small ball.
2. Roll out on to greaseproof paper.
3. To keep pastry intact, place a flan dish face down on to the greaseproof paper and invert it. Lightly press the pastry down and around the sides of the flan dish. Fill and bake as directed, depending on which recipe is used for the filling.

Buckwheat and Rice Bread G & W

Makes 14 slices (7 each loaf)

350 g (12 oz) buckwheat flour
175 g (6 oz) brown rice flour
1½ packets easy yeast
1 teaspoon sugar
15 ml (1 tablespoon) vegetable oil
½–1 tablespoon salt
300 ml (½ pint) hand-hot water

1. Mix together the flours and easy yeast.
2. Add the sugar, oil and salt, and mix to a thick batter with the water.
3. Grease and flour two 450 g (1 lb) loaf tins.
4. Divide the mixture between the tins, cover and leave to rise for 20–30 minutes.

5. Bake at 230°C (450°F) gas mark 8 for 35–40 minutes. The bread will contract slightly once cooked.
6. Cool for 5 minutes and turn out on to a wire rack.

Potato and Rice Bread G & W

Makes 16 slices (8 each loaf)

300 g (10 oz) potato flour
225 g (8 oz) brown rice flour
1½ packets easy yeast
1 teaspoon sugar
15 ml (1 tablespoon) vegetable oil
½–1 teaspoon salt
300 ml (½ pint) hand-hot water

1. Mix together the flours and easy yeast.
2. Add the sugar, oil and salt, and mix to a thick batter with the water.
3. Grease and flour two 450 g (1 lb) loaf tins.
4. Divide the mixture between the two tins, cover and leave to rise in a warm place for 20–30 minutes.
5. Bake at 230°C (450°F) gas mark 8 for 35–40 minutes. The bread will contract slightly from the sides once cooked.
6. Cool for 5 minutes and then turn out on to a wire rack.

Rice and Corn Flour Crispbread G W & Y

Makes 12 squares or 8 'Ryvita' size shapes

100 g (4 oz) brown rice flour
50 g (2 oz) cornflour
30 ml (2 tablespoons) oil of your choice
warm water to mix

1. Pre-heat the oven to 200°C (425°F) gas mark 7.
2. Mix ingredients together using enough water to make a soft dough.
3. Roll the dough out thinly on a surface dusted with flour. Cut into oblong biscuits and place on a greased baking tray.
4. Bake for 8–10 minutes.

Tapioca Crispbread G W & Y

Makes 12 squares

100 g (4 oz) milk-free margarine *or* vegetable fat
45 ml (3 tablespoons) water
pinch of salt
225 g (8 oz) tapioca flour
2 level teaspoons wheat-free baking powder

1. Pre-heat the oven to 180°C (350°F) gas mark 4.
2. Place the margarine or fat, water and salt together with one-third of the flour in a mixing bowl, and cream with a fork until mixed.
3. Sieve the remaining flour and the baking powder together and add to the mixture.
4. Knead very thoroughly until smooth.
5. Roll the dough out thinly on a lightly floured surface. Cut into squares and place on a greased baking sheet.
6. Bake for approximately 25 minutes.

Miss P's Punch G W & Y

Makes 1 litre (1¾ pints)

750 ml (1¼ pints) water
200 ml (⅓ pint) orange juice
50 ml (3–4 tablespoons) Ribena Light
2 yellow plums, chopped
2 red plums, chopped
1 orange, peeled, segmented and chopped
1 lemon, peeled and chopped
1 kiwi fruit, peeled and chopped
zest of 1 orange, peeled off in strips with a potato peeler
   or sharp knife

Mix all the ingredients together and serve chilled. This makes a refreshing drink with or between meals, especially if served with ice on a hot day.

RECOMMENDED READING LIST

GENERAL HEALTH

1. *The Vitality Diet* by Dr Alan and Maryon Stewart, price £4.95 (published by Thorsons). **UK A**
2. *Coming off Tranquillizers* by Dr Shirley Trickett, price £5.99 (published by Thorsons). **UK USA A** (Lothian Publishing Co.)
3. *The Migraine Revolution – The Drug-Free Solution* by Dr John Mansfield, price £4.99 (published by Thorsons). **UK USA A** (Lothian Publishing Co.)
4. *The Book of Massage* by Clare Maxwell-Hudson, price £10.99 (published by Ebury Press). **UK**
5. *Nutritional Medicine* by Dr Stephen Davies and Dr Alan Stewart, price £7.99 (published by Pan Books). **UK A**
6. *Pain-free Periods* by Stella Weller, price £4.99 (published by Thorsons). **UK**
7. *Osteoporosis* by Kathleen Mayes, price £4.99 (published by Thorsons). **UK**
8. *Beat PMS Through Diet* by Maryon Stewart, price £7.99 (published by Vermilion). **UK**
9. *Beat IBS Through Diet* by Maryon Stewart and Dr Alan Stewart, price £8.99 (published by Vermilion). **UK**

DIET

1. *Food Combining for Health* by Doris Grant and Jean Joice, price £4.99 (published by Thorsons). **UK USA A** (Lothian Publishing Co.)
2. *The New Raw Energy* by Leslie and Susannah Kenton, price £7.99 (published by Vermilion). **UK A** (Doubleday Publishing Co.)

3. *Foresight Index Number Decoder* (Packet Food Additive Dictionary), price £1.35 plus 20p p&p, available from Foresight (see Useful Addresses, page 203). **UK**
4. *The Reluctant Vegetarian Cook* by Simon Hope, price £14.95 (published by William Heinemann). **UK**
5. *The Single Vegan* by Leah Leneman, price £5.99 (published by Thorsons). **UK**
6. *Organic Consumer Guide/Food you can trust*, edited by David Mabey and Alan and Jackie Gear, price £4.99 (published by Thorsons). **UK USA A**
7. *Beat Sugar Craving* by Maryon Stewart, price £7.99 (published by Vermilion). **UK**
8. *Whole Earth Cook Book* by Hilary Meth, price £7.99 (published by Vermilion). **UK**
9. *The Wheat- and Gluten-free Cookbook* by Joan Noble, price £8.99 (published by Vermilion). **UK**

STRESS

1. *Self Help for Your Nerves* by Dr Clair Weekes, price £4.99 (published by HarperCollins, available 9 May 1995). **UK USA** (Hawthorn Publishing Co.) **A**
2. *Stress Wise* by Dr Terry Looker and Dr Olga Gregson, price £8.99 (published by Headway). **UK**

APPENDIX 2

USEFUL ADDRESSES

GENERAL HEALTH

Alcoholics Anonymous (AA)
General Services Office
PO Box 1
Stonebow House
Stonebow
York
YO1 2NJ
Tel: Stonebow (01904) 644026

ASH (Action on Smoking and Health)
109 Gloucester Place
London
W1H 4EJ
Tel: London (0171) 935 3519

College of Health
St Margaret's House
21 Old Ford Road
London
E2 9PL
Tel: London (0181) 983 1225

Eating Disorders Association
Sackville Place
44 Magdalen Street
Norwich
Norfolk
NR3 1JU
Helpline: (01603) 621414
Youth: (01603) 765050
Recorded Message: (0891) 615466

Food Watch Health Products Ltd
Pollards Yard
Wood Street
Taunton
Somerset
TA1 1UP
Tel: (01823) 325023

Foresight
Association for the Promotion of Pre-Conceptual Care
28 The Paddock
Godalming
Surrey
GU7 1XD
Tel: Godalming (01483) 427839

Friends of the Earth Ltd
26–28 Underwood Street
London
N1 7JQ
Tel: London (0171) 490 1555

Migraine Trust
45 Great Ormond Street
London
WC1N 3HZ
Tel: London (0171) 278 2676

Nutritional Health Ltd
PO Box 926
Lewes
BN7 2QL
Tel: Lewes (01273) 487366

Samaritans
General Office
10 The Grove
Slough
Berkshire
SL1 1QP
Tel: Slough (01753) 532713

The Shiatsu Therapy Centre
Kelvin Grove House
54 Kelvin Grove Street
Glasgow
G3 7SA
Tel: Glasgow (0141) 353 3477

The Soil Association
86–88 Colston Street
Bristol
BS1 5BB
Tel: Bristol (01272) 290661

WOMEN'S HEALTH

Association for Post-Natal Illness
25 Jerdan Place
Fulham
London
SW6 6RH
Tel: London (0171) 386 0868

Brook Advisory Centre
233 Tottenham Court Road
London
W1P 9AE
Tel: London (0171) 580 2911/323 1522

Miscarriage Association
c/o Clayton Hospital
Northgate
Wakefield
West Yorkshire
WF1 3JS
Tel: (01924) 200799

National Childbirth Trust
Alexander House
Oldham
London
W3 6NH
Tel: London (0181) 992 8637

The National Endometriosis Society
35 Belgrave Square
London
SW1X 8QD
Tel: London (0171) 235 4137

The National Osteoporosis Society
Barton Meade House
PO Box 10
Radstock
Bath
BA3 3YB
Tel: Bath (01761) 471771

Natural Family Planning Service
Catholic Marriage Advisory Council
Clitherow House
1 Blythe Mews
Blythe Road
London W14 0NW
Tel: London (0171) 371 1341

Pregnancy Advisory Service
11–13 Charlotte Street
London
W1P 1HD
Tel: London (0171) 637 8962

Wellbeing
27 Sussex Place
Regents Park
London
NW1 4SP
Tel: London (0171) 723 9296

Women's Health Information Centre
52 Featherstone Street
London
EC1Y 8RT
Tel: London (0171) 251 6580

The Women's Nutritional Advisory Service
PO Box 268
Hove
East Sussex
BN3 1RW
Tel: Hove (01273) 771366

ALTERNATIVE HEALTH

British Acupuncture Association
34 Alderney Street
London
SW1V 4EU
Tel: London (0171) 834 1012

British Homoeopathic Association
27a Devonshire Street
London
W1N 1RJ
Tel: London (0171) 935 2163

British School of Osteopathy
Administration and Clinics
1–4 Suffolk Street
London
SW1 4HQ
Tel: London (0171) 930 9254

The European School of Osteopathy
104 Tonbridge Road
Maidstone
Kent
ME16 8SL
Tel: Maidstone (01622) 671558

Institute for Complementary Medicine
Tavern Quay
London
SE16
Tel: London (0171) 237 5165

APPENDIX 3

NUTRITIONAL SUPPLEMENT SUPPLIERS

UK	*Supplies*
Name	
Efamol Limited Wharf House Wharf Road Guildford Surrey GU1 4RP Tel: Guildford (01483) 304441 (01483) 304437	Efamol.
Larkhall Natural Health/Greenfarm 225–229 Putney Bridge Road London SW15 2PY Tel: London (0181) 871 0401	A wide range of vitamins, minerals and specialised food including Trufree flour.
Nature's Best Health Products Ltd 1 Lamberts Road Tunbridge Wells Kent TN2 3EQ Tel: Tunbridge Wells (01892) 552117	A wide range of vitamins and minerals. Also Optivite.

Nature's Own
203–205 West Malvern Road   A wide range of vitamins
West Malvern   and minerals.
Worcs
WR14 4BB
Tel: Malvern (01684) 892555

Boots the Chemist
All branches.   Cream of Magnesia,
                                         Efamol.

Practitioners can buy Chromium GTF from Lamberts.

Australia
NNFA (National Nutrition Foods Association)
PO Box 84, Westmead, NSW 2145. (tel: 02 633 9913).
The NNFA have lists of all supplement stockists and retailers in
Australia, if you have any difficulties in obtaining supplements.
PMT Formula is available from **Blackmores**, 23 Roseberry Street,
Balgowlah, NSW 2093, Australia (tel: 02 949 3177).

New Zealand
NNFA (National Nutrition Foods Association)
c/o PO Box 820062, Auckland, New Zealand.
Again the NNFA have lists of all supplement stockists and retailers in
New Zealand, if you have any difficulties in obtaining supplements.
PMT Formula is available from **Blackmores**, 2 Parkhead Place, Albany,
Auckland (tel: 09 415 8585).

INDEX

ADVICE LINES
FROM THE WNAS

If you have enjoyed this book, you may also be interested in the following titles published by Vermilion:

BEAT PMS THROUGH DIET by Maryon Stewart	£7.99
BEAT SUGAR CRAVING by Maryon Stewart	£7.99
BEAT IBS THROUGH DIET by Maryon Stewart &	
Dr Alan Stewart	£8.99
THE NEW RAW ENERGY by Susannah &	
Leslie Kenton	£7.99
THE WHOLE EARTH COOKBOOK by Hilary Meth	£7.99
THE WHEAT- AND GLUTEN-FREE COOKBOOK	
by Joan Noble	£8.99

To obtain your copy, simply telephone
Murlyn Services on 0279 427203

You may pay by cheque/postal order/credit card and should allow
28 days for delivery. Postage and packing is free.